EL MEDICO
by Goya

DON QUIXOTE

OF

THE MICROSCOPE

An interpretation of the Spanish savant

SANTIAGO RAMON Y CAJAL

(1852-1934)

by

HARLEY WILLIAMS

JONATHAN CAPE
THIRTY BEDFORD SQUARE
LONDON

FIRST PUBLISHED 1954

PRINTED IN GREAT BRITAIN IN THE CITY OF OXFORD
AT THE ALDEN PRESS
BOUND BY A. W. BAIN & CO. LTD., LONDON

CONTENTS

CONTENTS

ILLUSTRATIONS

AUTHOR'S ACKNOWLEDGMENTS

To Dr. Luis Ramon y Cajal, son of the subject of this book, I am indebted for permission to quote from the original works in Spanish of Santiago Ramon y Cajal, of which his family owns the copyright. Of these works, I have used especially an English translation of Ramon y Cajal's autobiography, made with the help of Dr. Juan Cano by Professor Horne Craigie of the University of Toronto, one of Cajal's pupils. This excellent rendering has placed the master before a new world of readers. Dr. L. P. Eisenhart, Executive Officer of the American Philosophical Society (of Philadelphia), which far-sightedly published this book some twenty-five years ago, has, with Professor Horne Craigie, allowed me to use it freely as a source of information.

Professor Joseph Trueta, a graduate of the University of Barcelona, and now Nuffield Professor at Oxford, has generously advised me on the Spanish background. Mr. Norman Matheson, F.R.C.S., a staunch admirer of Ramon y Cajal, first prompted me to think of writing this book upon a personality in whom I had been interested for twenty years. To him, and to Dr. William McMenemey, who read a paper upon Cajal in 1953, I am grateful for much help.

Sir Henry Dale, O.M., has given me his recollections and advice.

Professor Wilder Penfield, O.M., of McGill University, Montreal, the most distinguished living pupil of Ramon y Cajal, has furnished me with first-hand impressions of the master.

AUTHOR'S ACKNOWLEDGMENTS

Sir Geoffrey Jefferson, F.R.S., has kindly allowed me to use papers by him dealing with the brain, and electronic computing machines

Dr. Robert L. Craig, on behalf of the New York Academy of Medicine, has authorized me to reproduce from the Journal of the Academy some examples of the *pensées* of Ramon y Cajal, as translated by the late Dr. Fielding H. Garrison.

Professor J. B. Trend, Professor of Spanish in the University of Cambridge, has permitted me to use material from his book *Origins of Modern Spain*, which gives an illuminating account of some leading Spanish personalities at the beginning of the present century.

Dr. Walter Pagel has helped me with notes upon Professor Waldeyer, of the chair of Anatomy in Berlin, as seen from the point of view of one of his students.

Dr. Alfred Coello has been consulted on points of detail, and drew my attention to an article by Pio Baroja.

Mr. Albert C. Gerould, Librarian of Clark University, Massachusetts, has lent me reports dealing with the visit of Ramon y Cajal to Clark.

Mr. Norman Cox, Dr. Robb-Smith of Oxford, Mr. Jo Pennybacker, F.R.C.S., of Oxford, Dr. Obrador Alcalde of Madrid, have helped me with information.

Dr. Cyril B. Courville has allowed me to make use of the translation of Cajal's *Precepts*, published under his editorship.

Dr. Xavier de Salas, Cultural Attaché to the Spanish Embassy in London, has been a source of strength and friendly inspiration throughout the writing of this book.

To any others, writers or publishers, to whom I have not written, or may be indebted without realizing the fact, I address apology and thanks.

AUCTORIS
SCRIPTORI
AMOR

'Everything in Spain has been done by the people, and what they did not do has been left undone. But a nation cannot consist solely of the common people: it needs an eminent minority. It is like a live body which consists not only of muscle but also of nerve ganglia and a cerebral centre. The absence of the "best people" or at least their scarcity, runs through our whole history and has kept us from ever being like other nations, a completely normal people.'

JOSÉ ORTEGA Y GASSET

'Whatever be the work we do, great or small, the essential thing is to do it with ardent affection.'

AZORIN

TO INTRODUCE RAMON Y CAJAL[1]

In the mountains of northern Spain a hundred years ago an impish schoolboy with a gift for drawing waged war with his father. The boy, Santiago Ramon y Cajal, wished to be a painter. His parent had other ambitions. The issue of this struggle between talent and discipline becomes the life of a biologist who found a new world — that of the ultra small. In one sense, the schoolboy never grew up. An impetuous desire for the impossible made him the veritable Don Quixote of science.

His training for a career was decidedly unorthodox. He who wanted only to use the pencil, found himself apprentice to barber, and then to a shoemaker. Even when his education was complete, he had to go through malaria and tuberculosis; by personal thrift he saved every peseta that was needed to buy his first microscope. Ramon y Cajal was over thirty before his scientific career opened; strangest of all, his real destination was displayed through that gift of drawing which had been so condemned in the unruly schoolboy. He became, in the course of time, winner of the Nobel prize, writer of wise and amusing epigrams, and a great European scholar. Yet he remained a patriot, as authentically Spanish as a melody of Granados, or a glass of sherry.

His own particular science, histology — the study of the tissues of the body — might prove daunting to anyone

[1] The name Ramon y Cajal is pronounced as a single word, with accents on the second syllables of both Ramon and Cajal. And in Spanish, the letter J sounds like an H, so Cajal is CAHAL.

not a specialist. The theme of this book is not histology, but Ramon y Cajal. In these pages his scientific work is described in non-scientific terms, as nontechnically as possible, as though with the innocent eye. Documents and references have been eliminated from the narrative, so that the qualities of this interesting man shall appear for their own sake. Everything that would look well on a tombstone has been sternly suppressed.

Biography treated in this spirit should reveal a man's universal quality, those features of his spirit and his life that would make an appeal to any human being in the world.

CHAPTER I

QUIXOTE OF THE MICROSCOPE

A SMALL boy of ten years old named Santiago
Ramon languished in an underground prison. A
century ago in Aragon, a period of juvenile
incarceration now and then was considered valuable
discipline. This boy was a most rebellious boy, and an
old offender. Yet he was not in the least cast down.
Being alone gave him time to think out further audacities
of the kind which had brought him to justice. Outside
in the town square his schoolfellows could be heard
shouting. He recognized their voices, their games,
everything that was going on. Though not depressed, he
dreamed, like every prisoner, that he was free, and
imagined those lively happenings in the sunshine outside — peasants with tall hats driving mules, soldiers,
priests, and the boys playing. Everything passed vividly
before his eyes in the darkness, and it took on colour as
brilliant as though he were free in the open air. That
scene became as perfect to his eyes as one of those
heavenly visions which the Holy Saints experienced when
in sorrow or affliction. Yet as he watched carefully the
procession of coloured figures as it moved across the
ceiling of the prison, he saw it was not imaginary, it was
definitely real. Those men and boys and donkeys
originated in a beam of sunshine that poured into the
darkness from a tiny hole in the shutter. How could
pictures be produced in this miraculous way? Santiago
Ramon was seized with curiosity.

He enlarged the hole in the shutter, and the pictures

became blurred. When he narrowed it again with a piece of paper, the outline of the moving panorama became sharp and clear once more. He was in rapture over his discovery. Perhaps no one in the world had ever seen such a thing before. Those hours of imprisonment went past all too quickly, as he experimented and pondered.

In that true episode which will be elucidated in a later chapter we have the whole spirit of the achievement of Ramon y Cajal; coolness in face of the marvellous; passionate absorption in what the eye could see; a gift for putting theories to the test. Those qualities were in time to make him, in the opinion of some Spaniards, their greatest countryman since Cervantes the creator of Don Quixote.

This boy became a man rather like Don Quixote: an adventurer, quite undeterred by warnings from conventional people; much given to attempting the impossible; a visionary, often over-rhetorical. And just as Don Quixote had a common, sensible Squire, Sancho Panza who deflated him and kept him from the worst blunders, so Ramon y Cajal was fortunate in having the counsel of a second personality — but inside himself. We shall see the two of them in operation. Quixote weaving sensational theories: Panza whispering — 'Come let's be practical', and helping him to realize them by hard work. Sometimes as we come to know his life, we may even feel that Sancho Panza is almost too strong. The hard worker seems to dominate the visionary knight. But Ramon y Cajal came from the north-east of Spain, where the people have the name for being cautious, frugal, good at business. Though our hero possessed all these characteristics, the visionary was the chief part of him. Let us see how he came to be in the world, and what sort of soil nourished his parents.

CHAPTER II

IN THE SIERRA

O N May 1st, 1852, at nine in the evening, was born Santiago Felipe Ramon y Cajal, the eldest child of the parish doctor, in a tiny township called Petilla de Aragon in the north-east of Spain. His mother had hardly ever left the mountains, but the father had travelled much — to Zaragoza and Barcelona. The soil of Aragon below their feet was more actual, more precious than any distant notion of Spain. They were Aragonese. To them the greatest of capitals was Barcelona on the coast of Catalonia near the mouth of the Ebro. If they thought of a city next in importance, it was more likely to be Paris than Madrid. The ancient realm of Aragon, which had belonged to the medieval federation of Catalonian states, was the basis of their patriotism. They would probably not have considered themselves as being Spanish at all.

This small hill town Petilla de Aragon, through a freak of feudal tenure, was actually a small island of Aragonese territory surrounded by the ancient Kingdom of Navarre. So that while Santiago's parents were Aragonese, he was, technically speaking, born a Navarrese. This fact intensified the stubborn and mountainous element in his background. It was indeed an austere land, a land of extremes. Around a hilltop, which had its ruined medieval keep, hung the village with thick defensive walls built against Goths and Moors. Stone houses, with low-pitched roofs made of curved tiles, looked as though they had budded out of the rock, and connecting the dwellings were narrow and precipitous lanes, mere passages between high walls, leading up to the church with its tower and bell. From the summit of the township, the eye could hardly see the neighbouring settlement, so completely did it merge into bronze-coloured lines of further rocky slopes, rising on a clear day to some snowcap in the jagged saw-edge of the Pyrenees. Only on becoming used to the landscape would one discern in the olive and tawny background, the roofs, zigzag walls and a belfry, those of another village seven miles away.

About the season when Santiago Ramon was born and for a few weeks in early summer, the land would become apple green, then copper green, as grasses and wild herbs burst forth after the melting of the snows. Goats fattened, cattle were turned out to feed, and everyone in the villages felt enraptured in the balmy air. The nights when the youths went courting, even to distant villages, were still cool, as they danced the *jota* to the tune of bagpipes, and the village square was full of extravagant costumes, billowing velvet skirts, lace aprons and shawls, and fantastic beaver hats of a shape traditional in each district.

Then the sun would show his power. Bright greens disappeared. Fields were burned dull umber and black and the rocks became indigo. Midsummer heat made each river a dry griddle of burning stones. A mood of lethargy took possession of these villages for several months. In October the early snow came, first on the peaks, then creeping lower and lower, accompanied by biting winds and deadly frosts, and these Aragonese would wrap themselves in long cloaks, and shiver over wood fires. Says the Spanish proverb: *Nueve meses de invierno y tres de infierno*: nine months of winter and three months of hell. That is the dominant rhythm of inland northern Spain, so opposite to the mildness of indolent Andalusia. Extremes of climate, mountain endurance, perpetual opposition to the whims and austerities of nature, such was the background of the doctor and his eldest, a child of the springtime when peasants believe the best are born. Their old stock was now and then capable of producing a savage flower of genius. Their ancient peasant qualities had engendered a modern scientist. For the fashioning of this miracle, however, we must take off our hats to the Aragonese village doctor, Justo Ramon Casasús.

In Spain a man keeps both his mother's and his father's name, but he places the father's name first and is called by it, or by both. The head of the Spanish State whom the world calls General Franco, is more formally Don Francisco Franco Bahamonde. The child of Justo Ramon and Antonia Cajal would be known formally as Santiago Ramon y Cajal, just as his father was Justo Ramon Casasús. In the village he was more familiarly, Santiago Ramon. Only when he became internationally famous did the scientific world, not appreciating a Spanish family custom, call him by the last name, his mother's. This allows us to make a convenient distinction. When we are thinking of the great scientist, we can say Cajal: but for the present, he is only a mountain boy Santiago Ramon, son of the village doctor of Petilla de Aragon.

This father, whom the people would call Don Justo, meaning respect thereby, was a remarkable personage, rather like a character of fiction, yet overflowing with life and will power.

CHAPTER III

DON JUSTO

JUSTO RAMON CASASÚS belonged to the generation which had been under the spell of the Bonaparte legend. He was himself a Napoleon of the sierras, a thick-set, dominating country doctor, with a good forehead, heavy mouth and brooding eyes. In a photograph taken by his son when the father was over seventy the face above the Gladstone collar, shows still the determination that was his greatest endowment and his legacy to his eldest son. As a practitioner he was a favourite with the people of the upper Aragon; a man rather more respected than beloved, demanding from his patients entire submission, and possessing a shrewd knowledge of human nature.

Few of the peasants of Petilla de Aragon who saluted the doctor as he rode by on his mule can have realized that he was essentially an unsatisfied, a disappointed man. His ambition burned like the July sun. He knew himself to be mentally superior to those wretched villagers with whom his lot was cast. Bitterness that he was no more than a country leech froze him like wind from the mountains. He was correct; Don Justo's talents were indeed superior to his role of doctoring peasants like those from whom he had sprung.

The parish doctor would receive a basic salary from the local *junta*, or Council, and the country people rewarded his services partly in corn, wood and eggs. They had greater faith however in their own essences, decoctions and poultices, than in the doctor's remedies which were invoked as a last resource. Richard Ford, the English traveller who visited Spain about the period when Justo Ramon was a young man, tells us of an ointment much esteemed in parts of Spain, the *Unto del hombre*. It was composed of human fat, taken from the region around the heart in a human corpse not yet cold. From such barbarities Don Justo struggled to escape.

In his work and in his ideas he represented what was rational and practical, and he was no friend to religion. He might be a familiar of the village priest — they and the clerk of the *junta* as the educated men of the locality would drink a glass of wine together. Yet as the doctor went his rounds, he felt himself to be the agent of a liberal mode of thought that belonged to a glorious future, and which would one day replace the miserable superstition that enslaved the majority.

Don Justo had done well for a man who started with nothing. As a boy, he left his own village to be a barber's apprentice, and read all the medical books his master possessed. At twenty-two, he took his wages and tramped to Barcelona, where he studied for a medical diploma while supporting himself by work in a barber's shop. With self-help, he succeeded, both in surviving, and being educated. By the time Santiago was born, the father had become a *practicante* — a member of the lower order of doctors who were permitted to attend simple illnesses and accidents. He dreamed of going still further, of being qualified as a regular physician, and one day, even a consultant, a member of the Faculty, in Zaragoza, or possibly Barcelona, greatest of all cities. Meanwhile the slowness of his ascent, and the lack of intellectual stimulus in these mountain villages irked him, as much as their poverty.

Ah, poverty, that was his nightmare; the fear of slipping back, falling to the level of a peasant without hope, a man who toiled over the soil. Don Justo was terrified of the possibility of losing his culture and the deference which they paid to a professional man. Worst of all, he literally dreaded hunger, of having to beg for his bread, of being despised and dependent. A Spaniard's emotions are not mild or moderate. He is a man of passionate extremes. Perhaps Justo Ramon over-emphasized the risks of his position in life, and, like many another self-made man, exaggerated the severity of his own struggle to rise. He communicated to his son both the ambition and the fierce joy that goes with accomplishment, though unhappily for many years, there was no sign of either to be noticed in the boy's behaviour.

At last, when Santiago was six years old, the father managed to take his University degree at Madrid. Now, he was able to move to wider and wealthier opportunities. From Petilla de Aragon, he migrated to Larres, from there to Luna an even more populous town, thence to Valpalmas. He was increasing the distance between himself and poverty, coming slowly nearer the centres of culture where he could further educate himself, and better prepare his sons. Eventually he landed in Ayerbe, a town of three thousand inhabitants, not far from the Provincial capital of Huesca. This for Don Justo was a considerable achievement. To his mind there were only two more cities worth conquering — Zaragoza the capital of Aragon, and beyond that, only Barcelona, queen of Catalonia. In Ayerbe, Santiago began his first school education, but his earlier training had already commenced under his father, in a singular and rigorous fashion.

Santiago developed early. When Don Justo was away in Madrid passing his examinations, he was pleased to get a home report from Ayerbe written by his six-year-old son, describing the state of his practice. Home tuition was increased, for Don Justo like all born teachers, brought into every lesson an element of self-instruction. The time came for learning French. So as not to be distracted by the noise of the home and the demands of his patients, Don Justo led his pupil to a most original schoolroom. It was a dry cave on a hillside, and there, sitting on a stone, the father and son laboriously construed *Telemache*, by Fénelon, a tale of imagined adventures which the seventeenth-century archbishop had written to amuse a Dauphin's son. When he was an old and famous man, Santiago Ramon y Cajal could remember in all its detail that pedagogic scene, more Homeric indeed than anything in the archbishop's narrative: the solitude of the cave, his father's face, the fantastic experiences of the boy prince Telemache, as the two of them forced their Iberian tongues around those French sentences.

At times in the following years when the father was most disappointed in his son he may have realized he was really being angry with himself. There in Santiago were failings which he had eradicated from his own nature; just as in looking in the mirror, he detected qualities that were lying undeveloped in his son and which could only be brought out through discipline.

Don Justo had a strong will, but no insight. It was some time before he could face the disagreeable truth that he had sired a dreamer. The boy had no desire to excel; he was potentially an idler and a failure. This was the doctor's firm and gloomy opinion. How were such infirmities of this young Quixote to be cured? Dr. Ramon was clear-headed and he was practical. There was need for perpetual strictness. No letting up of the pressure. His method henceforth was to train Santiago by submitting him to those same obstacles as he himself had successfully surmounted. When he knew what hardship was, Santiago would want to work hard in order to avoid it. A boy who realized what hunger meant, would make efforts so that he might not starve.

Saddened by the resistance he met with, yet meditating great things for his son, planning further ambitious thrusts for himself, despising his surroundings, dreaming of science, Don Justo Ramon rode his mule around Ayerbe, a fowling piece over his shoulder, a brace of partridges across the saddle that held his surgical instruments, and a textbook in his hand.

CHAPTER IV

MEMORIES

SANTIAGO went on his own way. He was indeed a dreamy, even an unsociable child. When he set out collecting birds' eggs, he went alone, having first paid out small bribes to the village children for reports of promising nests. At this stage in his scientific career, he had not mastered the technique of emptying the yolk, and his first collection was ruined. He loved woods, and the prospect of the sierra. He liked especially to wander by streams. For years, it was his dream to trace them back to their lairs in the mountains: the Aragon river, fed by the Gallego rushing down from the Pyrenees, and which in turn poured into the mighty Ebro that cuts across north-eastern Spain, and on to the sea. Out of an imaginative childhood Santiago treasured three main fragments. From such episodes we can read the history of an individual just as folklore teaches us the story of the race.

Spanish armies had won a great victory in Morocco, Tetuan had been captured, the Moors driven back, and the whole of Spain gave itself over to rejoicing, just as their forebears had done so many times during the previous thousand years over the reconquest of Spain from those hereditary enemies. Formerly the battles had been in the peninsula itself: now they were in North Africa. But the enemy was the same infidel, and they were the same Christians who had overcome the Muslim. In the village squares oxen were roasted over bonfires, wine-skins passed from mouth to mouth. In this explosion of patriotism the peasants of Ayerbe forgot their cares, drank themselves drunk, and danced to the thrumbling of strings and the wail of the pipes. Santiago remembered it all very vividly, and later on, Ramon y Cajal would enlarge that clear recollection of rejoicing in the square of Valpalmas into a strong emotion of pride, pride in being Spanish, and a resolve that Iberians should realize their gift for science.

Another afternoon as the schoolchildren of Valpalmas were saying the Paternoster under the eye of the school-mistress, the sky grew dark, and several claps of thunder deafened their voices. They had reached the solemn words 'Lord deliver us from evil' when an appalling crash shook the building, and the room was filled with dust and plaster. One boy rushed to the door, and in panic others followed. Out in the open air, they looked back and saw that part of the school was in ruins. Women rushed out from the houses, wiped dust from their faces, restored their morale, then, someone pointed up to the top of the church tower where a black object, like the effigy of a man, was hanging upside down. They ran up the steps and found the priest of the parish hideously injured by the bell which had fallen on top of him. In the hope of warding off disaster, or at least of warning his flock, he had climbed up to toll the bell which was then struck by the thunderbolt. The same electrical discharge which killed the priest had cut the school in half, rendering the mistress insensible. It had actually struck down off the wall a picture of the Saviour.

So fatal and extravagant an event made a deep impression throughout the countryside of Aragon in the year 1860. Calamity had spared the sinners but had destroyed the servant of God in His sacred place. It seemed a triumph of evil over good, and looking back upon that dramatic episode, Ramon y Cajal felt it was his earliest realization of tragedy.

In recollection, he traced the building up of his faith and intellectual confidence to another natural event which took place a little later. That fountain of universal knowledge, Don Justo, foretold that on a certain day, at a particular hour and minute during daylight, a black round shadow would actually pass across the sun. They would go to a hilltop and see it through smoked spectacles. Santiago was full of questions. How could such a happening be foreseen? Why did the moon come between sun and earth at that precise second? His father's answer was, Science. They climbed the hill, out came Don Justo's watch, and the eclipse occurred according to his programme. He pointed out that no other living creatures were allowed to share this scientific information. Birds were terrified, and hid their heads as though it were midnight. The whole of nature was discomposed, yet Don Justo was complacent. He had prophesied it all. For Santiago, the gravity, the inevitability of that event became a permanent memory. He pondered, doubted, was partly reassured. Those astronomers, who could so confidently announce an eclipse of the sun, as though they controlled the heavenly bodies with levers, they were not able to foresee the thunderbolt which killed the parish priest. Ramon y Cajal speculated upon nature, its immense variety, its inscrutable laws, and he traced his later intellectual development to the patriotic dancing, the thunderbolt, the eclipse. No doubt there was some artistic selection in those clear memories, so appropriately contrasted, so neatly fitting into the plan of his career. Perhaps this neat classification was the effort of an old man thinking back to the raw material upon which life had exercised its craft. In these memories he had faithfully recorded his three outstanding intellectual qualities: his fervent patriotism, his awe of nature, and his intense belief in the power of science to fertilize both. These elements were under the control of a Quixotic spirit that drew him to intellectual adventure.

Now he was to begin the process of higher education. If Santiago had foreseen the miseries of the next few years, he would have run away into the mountains.

CHAPTER V

DRAWING

RAMON pére had made another ambitious leap into a better practice and had landed in the market town of Ayerbe, in the centre of a wine-growing district, overtowered by a ruined castle built on a spur of the Pyrenees. It was the most urban and sophisticated place that Santiago had so far seen. Here the country folk thronged with butter, chickens, and vegetables two large squares. In the square of Ayerbe the doctor's son made his first real contact with that barbarous animal, the schoolboy.

They received him with a shower of stones. Their sharp eyes had detected something rustic in the style of his clothes. And his accent — it was definitely from the rural parts. To him, their dialect was equally uncouth, being made up of mispronunciations quite foreign to his experience, and afterwards identified as more Portuguese than Spanish. After this first painful rebuff, the new boy retired to lick his wounds. There was so much to see, the shop windows, the river, and the ruined castle. Boys were not necessary to him. Yet after his first relish of being alone, he felt once more the need to be with others. The gregarious part of his nature demanded to be satisfied. Santiago made his peace with the herd, adopted the boys' slovenly speech and joined with them in playing tops and quoits, fighting with fists, running and jumping. The idea of organized sports had not penetrated the province of Huesca in the 1860s, but these town boys had an excitement more thrilling than any ball game.

Near the town, the wealthy burghers raised grapes and peaches in gardens guarded by high walls. A handful of ripe figs tasted sweeter when gathered at night, after rival boys had been driven off with a shower of stones. The country bumpkin, not yet ten years old, forgot his desire for solitude, and threw his whole soul into this nocturnal warfare which the boys waged upon respectable Ayerbe. He was soon their resourceful leader. When tired of orchard robbing they followed the chase. Slings were made out of old wine-bottles, or when that supply failed, from the leather of their boots. Their arrows, tipped with spikes stolen from a shoemaker's awl, were made from the best wood, purloined with care. The long Spanish nights were glorious to them, and when there were no dogs and cats, they pursued rabbits and partridges. Parents, priests and policemen bewailed the regrettable wickedness of Ayerbe youth.

No more was Santiago Ramon in danger of becoming a morbid introvert. In the pursuit of an unlawful objective, and escape from the consequences, he had become outstandingly proficient. No other boy could climb a wall with his lizard-like ease, or discharge stones upon an enemy's head with such accuracy from the top of a walnut tree. When the police appeared he could retreat like an antelope. Yet even Santiago had his unpleasant experiences. Once he climbed an oak to seek a magpie's nest, and putting down his hand to feel for eggs, he met with something soft, but quickly withdrew. His fingers were covered with blood. Instead of magpies, he had encountered a colony of rats. Another escapade might have been more serious. He had climbed up rocks to find an eagle's nest, and was trapped on the face of the cliff, unable to move up or down. Only after he had cut steps with his knife was he able to find his way to safety. Santiago Ramon came to be looked on by teachers as an exceptionally unpromising lad, and each day, on coming home from his rounds Don Justo would hear of some fresh wickedness. On one occasion, to escape his wrath, Santiago and his younger brother ran away from home and hid for days. Eventually their father tracked them down: they were sleeping in a lime-kiln. As he drove them home ignominiously through the streets like stray sheep, Dr. Ramon reflected bitterly that he had produced the town terror of Ayerbe, and stormed at his wife for her softness. We do not hear much of Antonia Cajal, expect for the tenderest feelings she inspired in her boy, and we can be sure she often protected him from the father's anger. It was she who endowed him with the other and more important part of his genius, artistic sensibility. Justo Ramon had as much sensibility as an empty goatskin.

The disciplinarian father probably regarded this orchard robbing as inevitable. As an old man, Ramon y Cajal looked back on his escapades as expressions of a child's constant need for sugar to supply his enormous discharge of physical energy. To his backward glance, stealing grapes was a bodily craving rather than a moral transgression. In Don Justo's eyes, however, the boy had another failing, much more ominous. It was a most deplorable tendency. It stared at the doctor a dozen times a day. Santiago was addicted to drawing and painting. The margin of every book was covered with men, horses, castles. Each house wall was a background for battles and bullfights. To colour these detestable pictures, he would extract the colour from plaster, he would even steal his father's coloured cigarette papers to soak out the dye. No one knew where he found the brushes. This atrocious habit filled the doctor with foreboding. He did not remember, or did not know, that the great painter Francisco Goya y Lucientes was a native of Aragon and had had a most successful career which opened in a similar way. In matters of art, Don Justo was blind and deaf, for to his rational mind, being an artist was the same thing as being a failure. He shuddered to think of his own boy dreaming and drinking all day in a café, sinking lower and lower, becoming at last a shiftless vagabond. There was one practical remedy— to forbid pencils at once.

It is interesting that in the 1860s a veritable mania for drawing and painting seemed to spread over Spain. In the art schools of Paris and Rome, Spanish students were disproportionately numerous, and the four academies of the Peninsula were full. Don Justo may have known personally some of the failures. That amount of credit may be given him for the measures he now took. He had no insight into his boy's gifts, and no glimmering of the fact that this talent which now he resolved to eradicate was destined in the end to crown the career he had mapped out for Santiago.

The child, he was hardly ten, who could extract a peach from an orchard without making the leaves rustle, was quite able to acquire forbidden materials for his prohibited hobby. Charcoal could be made, pencils stolen, prayer books had margins, and every expanse of white wall was a standing invitation. In illiterate Spain, pictures on walls were the instinctive mode of popular expression. Santiago lost himself in pictorial fancies. Roman soldiers covered with armour fought warriors on horseback. Greek athletes struggled with lions, and triremes sailed the seas. He especially enjoyed religious themes. He drew his patron, Saint James, in a gamboge helmet and long black beard fighting off the Moors with a dark blue sword, while infidel corpses lay around in abundance. Though contemporary scenes did not really attract Santiago, he would occasionally draw a house, or a church, or a peasant pouring wine down his throat from a glass *porron*.

One day Don Justo saw a new manifestation of the boy's mania — it happened to be Saint James once again, and he made a decision. His own warnings had not been effective. He would now invoke the thunders of the most exalted authority on matters of art. This expert happened to be the town plasterer of Ayerbe who also attended to frescoes in the churches and touched up the colours of the murals. To this journeyman, as though to an artist of the highest standing, he showed his son's drawings. No doubt winks and a gratuity passed between them as the doctor inquired: 'Does this show any talent for drawing?', and the anguished Santiago kept his eyes on the man's face.

The decorator put on a jeering expression. He scoffed at defects of proportion. What sort of hand was that given to the Holy Apostle? The horse's head — it might have been made of wood. Dr. Ramon's further leading questions produced even more crushing replies. Poor Santiago was utterly humiliated, and the father who in spite of his vehemence, had perhaps secretly hoped for a different result, was angry too. In his simplicity he had expected an authoritative opinion from the town plasterer, but now his worst fears had been confirmed. He must take further repressive measures. He set himself more assiduously to cure this failing. No more pencils.

Charcoal was forbidden like a sin. But his eldest boy was also a Ramon. He was never seen with a pencil, yet drawings flowered like violets in secret.

Modern handling of such a situation would indeed be different. How flattered a parish doctor would be today at any hint of talent in his son. Find him an art school, a scholarship, a studio, give the boy every encouragement! Modern children are all geniuses, and a proud father would be more likely to magnify a gift. That was not the path by which Santiago Ramon developed his instinct for drawing and used it in the service of his science. His capacities grew in the harshest soil. His Quixote achievements belong to the realm of the unlikely and impossible. Don Justo's resolve to eradicate the desire to draw made it more tenacious, yet gave it a different twist. That humiliating experience with the decorator was one of those shocks that to mediocrity mean extinction, but direct genius into its right channel. Santiago learned to renounce the fantastic and exploit the actual. His artistic gift thus diverted was drawn towards realism. In the greenhouse of child-guidance he might have become a fluent executant with a pleasing small-scale talent. Under the fierce parental opposition his gift grew deep roots, it became a great Spanish oak, of splendid timbers, and rich in shade.

Both father and son came away from the talk with the plasterer in a chastened mood. The boy was thoughtful yet dismayed. Outwardly he continued to rebel, yet inwardly he acquiesced. Though he could no more help using a pencil than throwing a stone, he obeyed his father to the extent of renouncing altgether all hope of a painter's career. He would paint, but he would not be a painter. Half consciously, he made a psychological bargain with his father. This ambivalent attitude to Don Justo — one of accommodation to a superior force balanced by secret fulfilment of his own desires — became the ground plan of Santiago's mental growth during the next ten years.

CHAPTER VI

VISION IN CAPTIVITY

THE final episode of his schooldays in Ayerbe, that of his vision in the school prison, has been described already. Spain is a land where visions and prisons play a large part in the lives of great men, but Santiago's experience has a modern touch, since the hallucination developed into a scientific experiment. He had been more rash than usual in handing around the class some caricature of the teacher, and an outburst of laughter infuriated the master. He had stood enough from young Ramon. This was the end. The boy was marched off to the underground room, overrun with mice, with only one shuttered window. He was by no means in a chastened mood. All his senses were alert, and when the magic-lantern pictures appeared on the ceiling, he had the presence of mind to work out how it came to be, and the mental ingenuity to test his own conclusions.

To the end of his life, Ramon y Cajal cherished that memory, and naturally he romanticized it. With the years, he came to believe he had actually rediscovered the phenomenon of the *camera obscura* which is really the basis of photography. The ceiling of the prison corresponded to the photographic plate, the size of the hole was, by accident, perfectly proportioned to the focal distance, and a pencil of sunshine in the dark room did the rest. With permissible pride Ramon y Cajal gives us in his memoirs the impression that the boy Santiago had divined the laws of optics which made possible this visual marvel. We may take this with a grain of salt; and as for priority — Leonardo da Vinci and others had been there before, and had produced pictures in dark rooms. The real originality lay in his impulse to try out the effect of enlarging and narrowing the hole. Most Spanish boys would not have gone beyond the idea of a supernatural visitation, and would never have thought of so testing it. Santiago's performance throws a beam of illumination upon the beginnings of his scientific curiosity.

This happening in the school prison at Ayerbe was as significant in Cajal's life as another and very different vision that came to Ignatius Loyola in the cave at Manresa.

CHAPTER VII

FRAY JACINTO

DISSATISFIED with the progress his son was making at the local school, Don Justo Ramon decided to send him to be under the Aesculapian fathers at the *Schola Pia* in the old capital city of Jaca, further up in the mountains. The establishment had a reputation for Latin and discipline. It was arranged that Santiago would lodge in the house of an uncle who kept a weaver's shop, and who owed a debt to Don Justo. This neat boarding arrangement was the father's notion of getting back value for his loan, and it throws small credit upon him. His money was to be repaid in his son's misery and ill health. Jaca was a very ancient place, up near the Basque country and they travelled to it in a rough cart. Santiago's tears at parting from his mother dried up in the excitement of wonderful scenery. They followed the river Gallego flowing now through a ravine, then in a broad valley, and Dr. Ramon had many stories to tell of battles in the Carlist war, and Santiago learned that it was from these parts that his own mother came. Jaca itself, the medieval centre of Aragon, was a place of brooding traditions where at one time, so the legend was, murderers were buried alive beside their victims. They came to the Aesculapian College, and Dr. Ramon in presenting his son to Father Jacinto, a burly muscular monk who had a ferocious name for breaking in difficult boys, said he hoped no pains would be spared to root out this madness of drawing. As Santiago observed the

teacher's huge fists and broad shoulders his private
resolutions were neither peaceable nor submissive.

The uncle's home in Jaca was poverty stricken. How
did Don Justo fail to notice? Catering was left to an old
servant who fed Santiago mainly on tasteless gruel and
apples. Even the stew that came on Saints' days contained very little meat, and the wretched boarder found
that his helping was mostly thin soup. Real hunger and
he now became acquainted, and he used to cheat it by
roasting potatoes and eating them secretly.

The teacher of Latin, Don Jacinto Villan, of the Order
of St. Francis de Paul, was not greatly different from
other educators of a hundred years ago in believing that
learning is never acquired without stripes. But his
disciplinary methods went far beyond the custom. He
terrified the little boys with his stentorian voice as he
made them memorize their conjugations. Any stumbling
was visited with the leather strap. On one occasion he
punched a pupil so hard that he fell backwards seven
feet against a blackboard which came down on the heads
of two other boys. In this College there was a prison, a
punishment book, and a whip of many lashes. For very
serious offences, there was a further degradation called
'King of the Cocks', in which the boy victim was dressed
in feathers and made to run up and down between lines
of boys who thrashed him. To encourage a spirit of
competition, the class was divided into Romans and
Carthaginians, Santiago being among the latter, and on
days when he was not punished by the violent Fray
Jacinto, he was beaten by the victorious Romans.

He was being starved, of food, of friendship, of human
understanding, and cruelty had its usual consequence.
Blows sounded in his head like those of a door knocker in

an empty house. Santiago's power of verbal recollection
(as in the case of many intelligent boys), had never been
as good as his other faculties, and now, the bellowing of
Father Jacinto, against which he was inadequately
fortified by the effect of the corn porridge, took away
what memory he had. His Latin grew worse, and he
came to feel crushed and hopeless. His only outlet was
to decorate margins of his missal with arabesques and
sketches, wishing the margins were more spacious.

When the teacher saw he was producing no effect he
changed his tactics, but not in the direction of greater
leniency. Systematic starvation must now be applied.
Santiago was put into the school prison over the dinner
hour when other boys were in the refectory. But this boy
had a way with locks and bars, and he soon managed to
escape and find his way to the monks' kitchen where he
helped himself. Once, when through absent-mindedness
of one of the fathers, he was left locked up for a day and
a night, he emerged from the prison, and by descending
one wall and climbing another, turned up for dinner at
his uncle's. Escaping became a habit, in fact an art, but
unfortunately other boys learned to imitate him and Santiago's further plans were frustrated.

Between bouts of Latin prose, prison-breaking and
encounters with Fray Jacinto, he would go solitary walks
along the banks of the river Aragon. It became like an
artery running through his soul, as he sat to sketch the
outline of the hills, the birds, the ripples on the surface
of the water, dreaming how this magic stream, born high
up in the Pyrenees, rushed on to join the mighty Ebro.
The young patriot of eleven longed to trace it back to
some crystal loch near the Col de Ladrones among the
rainbows. He set out and walked for hours. Then a

shepherd told him he was still many leagues from the summit, and with sadness he turned back, home to the Aesculapian Fathers and Latin grammar.

School reports that went home to Ayerbe were bad, and at last Don Justo saw he had made a mistake. He took the cart once more up the Gallego, and brought his boy home from Jaca.

The Ramon strain in Santiago had managed to resist that system of ignorant brutality. He was in fact made of tougher material than his teacher, for Fray Jacinto's violence ruined his arteries and carried him off at the age of forty-four from a cerebral haemorrhage. Upon Santiago the effect of harsh discipline was definite and on the whole, not destructive. It made him more resourceful, more inventive, less willing to conform. Quixote's dreaminess was blended with the wisdom of Sancho Panza and that dual character became the source of his power.

We can imagine the tears of horror when Donna Antonia saw her boy's thin cheeks and pointed chin after his return at Jaca, and we may trust that she expressed her feelings to Dr. Ramon. Under the influence of good food and family reassurance Santiago soon recovered. His first holiday occupation was to manufacture a cannon, for in his absence, the technique of warfare among the boys of Ayerbe had progressed from the era of the bow and arrow into that of gunpowder. Without an effort, Santiago resumed his former leadership and appointed himself maker of cannon. He forced a hole down the centre of a log and bound up the outside with wire. No doubt he had seen pictures of early pieces of ordnance, and this cannon resembled one of those primitive weapons. It was carefully carried to a garden wall, filled with bits of iron and stones, rammed with home-made gunpowder, and trained on a neighbour's gate which happened to have been newly painted green. The impatient boys wished to open fire at once; but Santiago restrained them while he calculated each angle like a military engineer. Not until he was satisfied was the fuse lit.

From a safe distance, they heard a magnificent report, and through the dust of the explosion they saw with a thrill of triumph a huge hole in the neighbour's newly painted green gate. Then they heard the neighbour's shouts. He could not reach them because of the wreckage but began to throw stones, and the boys scattered quickly. The cannon had been an undoubted success.

It was obvious to the elders of Ayerbe that this display of ballistics had coincided with Santiago's return from Jaca, and that his was the master mind. Once more, he found himself in duress, this time under the *Alcalde* or Town Mayor in a real prison, with cockroaches and mouldy straw. To put himself right with the Mayor, Dr. Ramon himself had suggested his favourite remedy — a sharp period of starvation. This was carried into effect, though secretly defeated by Senora Ramon who sent in to the prison pies, biscuits and fruit. Like Cervantes, like Camoens, and even the gentle St. John of the Cross, Santiago became acquainted with the meaning of genuine imprisonment, the destiny of most Spanish individualists. Four days in the municipal lock-up at Ayerbe were not marked this time by any scientific visions. When he came out, he resumed his experiments with firearms.

Don Justo possessed an old flintlock which was never fired, but was kept at home for a particular purpose. In that period of wars and rebellions through which Spain was passing, the police made a frequent practice of commandeering all privately owned guns until the particular emergency was over. The doctor of Ayerbe did not care to be deprived of his field sports, so he kept this ancient fowling piece specially in order to hand over to the Civil Guard, while he continued his shooting with a more effective weapon.

The boys purloined the flintlock, filled it with powder. and amused themselves. But the spluttering of the saltpetre and the squeaking of the lock were enough to scare any bird. Santiago's last vacation at Ayerbe passed off harmlessly. A further item in the educational programme was due.

CHAPTER VIII

HUESCA

HE was sent to the capital of the Province, Huesca, to what in England would be called a high school. The city had been the Roman town of Ossa and its cyclopean ring of walls had ninety-nine towers. Santiago delighted in the atmosphere, the historical background, and the beautiful things he could record with a new box of paints which he bought immediately. The marble reredos of the Cathedral had arabesques which might have been woven by fairies. In the crypt of one of the churches was an ancient bell by which Kings of Aragon had summoned their Knights to drive out the Moors from Huesca. In a boarding-house where the boy lodged, were young priests and theological students who could answer his questions about history. After the drabness of Ayerbe, the larger shops and cleaner streets of Huesca made him feel he was truly in a centre of culture and elegance.

The teacher of Latin, in the Institute of this wonderful place, was old and of failing eyesight, the very opposite of the terrible Fray Jacinto. Every trick which the fiendish ingenuity of boys has ever practised on an incompetent master was played on this unfortunate man. Mice leaped between the desks, bats and birds soared in the classroom, the old man's spectacles were drawn away by an invisible thread — while pandemonium reigned. Santiago might have taken his revenge for his treatment at Jaca. Yet the opportunity when it came, seemed pointless. He had suddenly matured. These rowdy

amusements came to seem stale. By contrast, there was a
geography master who had the gift of effortless discipline
merely because he inspired the boys. Santiago began to
draw maps. He learned the glories of the Spanish
Empire which had stretched from Cape Horn to San
Francisco. His visual faculty, his strongest gift, was
stimulated.

The young *hidalgos* of the Huesca Institute were as
particular about dress as the boys of Ayerbe. When the
undersized Santiago first appeared, their eyes fastened
unerringly on his overcoat. It had belonged to the
doctor, had been made over by Senora Ramon, and was
rather too long to suit the taste of these schoolboy
stylists. One boy, over-sized, nineteen and stupid,
shouted: 'Dago, where's your harp and monkey?'
Whereupon Santiago sprang on him like a leopard, but
in a few minutes all the others were on top of him. In the
end, he was obliged to creep home, sore and vanquished
with the atrocious word 'Dago' in his ears, and revenge
in his heart. If only he could tackle that bully, he would
have the whole school at his feet. Pride made him
resourceful. He began secretly a course of physical
training.

Each day in the woods he practised strenuously,
climbing trees, lifting stones, jumping. Perfection did
not come as quickly as he hoped, but he persevered, by
a method that was to be useful later on. He put his whole
soul into the pursuit, over-valuing his objective for the
time being, and using a degree of effort which overwhelmed resistance. At last after many months came
the victorious moment when he could take on the strong
boy. Then to his surprise, he found that to possess
superior strength means that it need not be used. That

overgrown peasant with thick neck and ploughman's arms sensed the change in the little fellow, and he became respectful, even friendly. The overcoat was never mentioned. Santiago's physical efforts had been translated into moral terms.

His craze for being the strong man lasted several years; and one of the few occasions when he received his father's wholehearted approval was due to this monkey-like agility. The Ramon family had come home late from the theatre, to find they had forgotten the key of the front door. Whereupon the athlete of Huesca and the prison-breaker of Jaca swarmed up the side of the house and entered by a balcony. No doubt Don Justo suitably concealed his satisfaction that this worthless son of his had at last been able to do something really useful.

CHAPTER IX

THE DICTIONARY OF COLOURS

THROUGH chinks in the shutters of a Spanish house beams of the morning sun filter into the room and cast a gridiron of light on the walls. It is still dark, yet something else is about to be born. Then, the shutters are opened, and a new world comes to life, a morning world, when even sunshine is bearable and the air fresh, the time when each of the senses awakens once more. With the same sudden flood of illumination, Santiago's imagination was aroused. It was not yet love, but it was something very near to love, the world of beauty.

For years he had practised with the pencil, so as to become fairly competent, and he used colours in a routine fashion to fill the outlines. Then, abruptly, with an almost painful shock, each colour in nature broke up into a dozen different depths he had never noticed before. He was amazed, challenged. That coarse green which was daubed on church frescoes, the indigo he had always favoured for the Holy Apostle's beard — each shade of paint was quite inadequate, unnatural. When he painted directly from nature, his awakened eye informed him that every tone should be different. Grass, oak leaves, the olive and the pine, each represented a separate modulation of green, yet on his paper they all looked the same. He faced this new situation with resourcefulness that has a scientific flavour. To remember those shades in the spectrum, and to be certain of reproducing the one he needed, he compiled a reference book, a catalogue of colours, each tint graded and numbered, and corresponding to some natural object. Santiago Ramon began that inspiring, yet heartbreaking pursuit of copying many differently coloured flowers. Each example was to serve as an item in his catalogue.

Yet in spite of this newly awakened aesthetic maturity, he was still the wild boy underneath. A specimen of a flower seemed richer if it had been snatched from danger. To furnish his dictionary of shades, our young perfectionist of twelve years old needed one particular rose. No other species of rose would do. It had to be the variety known as 'the rose of Alexandria', and it grew only in one private garden surrounded by a high wall. To ask for a specimen, by going up to the front door, was unthinkable. That would have compromised the high artistic purpose. This coveted rose had to be raped in darkness from that magic garden where it blossomed secretly. With two companions, Santiago scaled the wall and dropped down inside. Immediately two gardeners armed with heavy sticks appeared and began to chase them.

The exit was locked, and the boys were pursued, round and round. Each minute it became hotter and more dangerous. The men were closing in and their cudgels getting nearer. Then, one of the boys tripped, and was set upon. Santiago snatched this respite to leap and catch the branch of an apple tree and gain the top of the wall. He showered stones upon the men who had meanwhile captured both other boys. Santiago escaped unidentified, but his companions were absent from school for several days on account of the beating they got from the gardeners.

Complacently, in remembering that exciting episode

later on, Ramon y Cajal asked: 'What schoolboy today would risk his skin merely for the pleasure of possessing a rose and enriching an album?'

His pride was justifiable, though he expressed no sympathy for his less agile companions. His was the peasant's belief in toughness, and he never complained of punishment. The Quixote longed for danger and difficulty, but Sancho Panza had enabled him to seize the branch and escape with a whole skin. That dictionary of colours contained one vital shade that does not belong to the spectrum, the colour of excitement and calculated danger. We have to think of Cajal always as two blended characters: the careful copyist who spared no pains to render the object he studied, who over-valued, over-intensified each thing until it was complete. There was also the reckless adventurer who valued nothing unless it was nearly impossible, who instinctively chose for his researches the toughest, the most inscrutable theme.

CHAPTER X

ROBINSON CRUSOE

DON JUSTO scanned a critical school report upon the winter's work at the Huesca Institute. It was as bad as he feared. But now, the summer holidays of 1864 had begun. There was a chance to make up for some of the time which had been lost. If Santiago would not work at school, he would be made to work at home. The father laid down a rigid programme of lessons to be followed each day. Did Santiago understand that his father was serious and would expect him to work hard to catch up? Yes, he did. As usual, Santiago bowed to the storm. Then he made a proposal that was so unexpected that Don Justo was quite nonplussed and could not find a reason for refusing. High up at the back of the house there was an unused pigeon shed, which was above the level of the neighbouring roofs. Here, Santiago pointed out plausibly, he would be able to get peace, undistracted by disturbance from his brothers. Concentration upon his lessons would come more easily there in the shed. On the spur of the moment Dr. Ramon could not think of any coherent objection. In his habitual groove, he was a shrewd man; away from it, he was very gullible. He gave his consent to the pigeon house, and Santiago became installed in a masterly strategic position. Through the open door he could keep watch, and it was easy to hide underneath a pile of books his unauthorized paint-box and drawings, for he meant to enjoy that summer holiday. He could have had no idea how truly significant those few weeks were to be in the development of his mind. From the shades of the pigeon house he was to set forth on a voyage of exploration equivalent to the discovery of the Indies.

As he came to investigate his surroundings, he found he overlooked the attic window of the neighbour, who happened to be a pastry-cook. There through the window he could see rows of trays spread with cakes and tarts. He soon invented a way of entering that room, early in the morning before the family were awake. Though no more than twelve, he was old enough to have tasted hunger, and he knew that forbidden fruits are the sweetest. He was also boy enough to believe that present pleasure is better than future gain. His eyes wandered round the walls of the attic. He was calculating how often he could break into that room without being detected, when he saw that against the walls were piles and piles of books, he had never seen so many books. He opened one of them and began to read.

Don Justo's notion of literature was, like his idea of art, severely utilitarian. Books were good only if they were practical, and offered facts. He would have on his own shelves only works of science and mathematics, those which contained exact knowledge that could be used. Philosophy, or fiction (to him they were the same) were pernicious. He frowned upon the few novels which his wife kept hidden in the bottom of a trunk. The children had never read any poetry, except some ballads sold by hawkers. To Santiago, therefore, practically all books were forbidden books. Yet as he looked around the walls of the pastry-cook's attic, he saw titles which he had heard grown-ups mention. He recognized *Robinson Crusoe, Don Quixote*, the *Three Musketeers*, there were many others he had never heard of, and they represented a fascinating unexplored world. Then he gazed once again at the trays of cakes.

In the middle of the room, the boy stood undecided. He opened another book and longed to read it. This would take time, and he reasoned he would have to make many visits to read all these books. He made up his mind. No one would notice or care, were he to take the books away, one at a time. But cakes would certainly be counted, and if he were to steal even one, his scheme of reading was doomed. He made up his mind with heroic resolve. With his mouth still watering, he decided to leave the cakes alone, and to borrow one book, discreetly returning it before he took the next. For that whole summer, the confectioner's upper room became his lending library. Imagination had triumphed because it was fresh and strong.

We can admire the self-sacrifice of a boy of twelve as well as his ingenuity. Each dawn he would enter the attic, take what he wanted from the shelves, and leave the tarts severely alone. His father had no suspicions of the disciplined strategy of that summer campaign of reading. The boy was quiet up in the pigeon house — better there than to have him roaming the streets and stealing peaches, and the confectioner never realized he was feeding the liveliest imagination in Ayerbe.

That pastry-cook had good taste in literature, and had collected the great romantic authors as their works appeared. Never in the whole history of books were there writers so likely to appeal to the imagination of a boy. Balzac had been in his grave only twenty years, but Alexandre Dumas was writing still. There was Victor Hugo, and Chateaubriand; the boy dipped into them as instinct guided, choosing writers he fancied most. As formerly he longed for grapes and figs, now he satisfied hunger and thirst with the sublime and terrible things men and women did on paper. Tales about imaginary people became more alive than his actual experience. Among these classics there was one book that expressed— more than anything he was ever to read in the whole of his life— Santiago's ideal. This was the story of Robinson Crusoe. Even the initials were those of his own name— Ramon y Cajal.

Here was a cool and resourceful man who treated danger with detached curiosity, whose shipwreck on the desert island gave a chance for his plan of calculated resource. What a man, what an opportunity. The literal exactitude of that book charmed Santiago as it has done every other reader since its appearance in 1719. The hero's skill in preserving his gunpowder in little packets for safety; the oil lamp he made from goat's tallow; the grains of corn he saved for four years before ever he had a loaf of bread to eat— the boy of twelve understood everything. Those things were just what he would have done himself. He too had imagined such adventures, and henceforth he would model himself even more closely upon Robinson Crusoe. The craftsmanship of the desert island became a lifelong inspiration.

To a Spanish boy, Don Quixote might be expected to appeal, yet compared with Crusoe's triumphal victory over his surroundings, the irony of the other career was a disappointment to Santiago. It needed experience of life to comprehend so sad and subtle a reaction to misfortune. Later on, like every Spaniard, Cajal was to psychologize about this classic, but so far his own Quixotism had not yet matured. For the present, he was content to be Robinson Crusoe.

He began to write out a long romance of his own, about a desert island and the life that was lived there. As the story grew, he shared it secretly with other boys, and they decided to make their romance real. In the river at Ayerbe there was a genuine island sufficiently savage, and their imagination easily made it remote. There the boys encamped, daubing themselves with mud. They crossed in a boat, and lived in a stockade and solemnly they took an oath that if they were to fail to pass their school examinations, they would run away from home and live on the Crusoe island for ever. But one of the other boys could not bear the burden of that ruthless resolve. He told the dreadful secret to his parents, and they had a good laugh. Somehow it spoiled the delicious atmosphere of hardship and adventure. Santiago cancelled the expedition.

We have been proud for him over the quest of the rose of Alexandria. We admire his fortitude in deciding not to touch the cakes. Now we can be glad for his sake that this high-mindedness brought him to the island of fantasy, and an understanding of his own pioneer qualities. One of those same schoolboys, who became later a celebrated criminologist, said of Ramon y Cajal that his real achievement in life was to surpass Daniel Defoe and use the microscope to discover a realm even more fantastic than Crusoe's island.

CHAPTER XI

APPRENTICESHIP

DON JUSTO'S ambition for his eldest son, however much it was inspired by pride and self-fulfilment, had always the dark tinge of fear. Suppose, after all, this boy were to prove unworthy and incapable? Were to turn out an idler? Worse still, if he were to be orphaned and thus deprived of a father's salutary discipline? In such pessimistic moments, the doctor had better hopes of his second boy Pedro who was turning out to be everything he could wish for. If only Santiago could be as amenable and hardworking as his younger brother. A blind spot in his sympathies prevented the doctor from perceiving the unusual gifts that Santiago was developing under his very nose. He was even more wide of the mark as to the real character of the dutiful Pedro, as will appear.

After that summer holiday, school reports continued to be bad, and perhaps Don Justo found out the secrets of the pigeon house. Whatever was the cause — he now made an extraordinary decision. Next term, when Santiago returned to Huesca, the father arranged for him to be apprenticed to a barber, and to live in his master's house above the shop. The object was to keep him out of mischief in his spare time and less likely to exercise a bad influence over Pedro. Don Justo himself had started life stropping razors, and thought it good that his son should have to go through the hardships from which he himself had emerged so triumphantly. There was of course a traditional connection between barbers and surgeons, and in the nineteenth century apprenticing a boy to a master was the usual method of vocational training. This much, at least, we can say in Don Justo's favour — and, for the present, suspend judgment upon this new twist in his educational policy.

The following term, after his holiday of romance, Santiago found himself assistant to a certain Señor Acisclo, in a street near the Cathedral, much discouraged by the change. He began to learn to attend to razors and hold the brass bowl to the chins of priests and shop-keepers while the master performed his art.

In old Spain a barber's saloon was a townsmen's club. The whitewashed walls were hung with pictures of bullfights and pretty girls. Customers with shaggy hair and dark chins threw dice and sold lottery tickets while they waited their turn on the bench underneath a statue of the Holy Virgin. Everyone talked of politics and love; and the barber himself was not only a great performer with the razor, but also a gifted guitarist, and a recognized arbiter among the Don Juans of Huesca. In this trade, a man had to be an entertainer and minor surgeon as well; Señor Acisclo did a little bloodletting and probably gave medical advice too. He was pleased with his new pupil. 'Santiago, my boy, if you only listen to me, you will grow up into a splendid barber, in time, and think of the wages, and the tips!' The boy began to get over his disappointment. The barber's saloon was a place where one saw everything that was going on, and met the leading characters of Huesca. For a boy of thirteen, what he heard was most exciting. Fights with knives, nocturnal wooings through iron-barred windows, escapes from jealous husbands — there were matters upon which the barber had to adjudicate,

and despite occasional storms of temper, he was kind to
Santiago, and allowed him a degree of freedom that
entirely frustrated the rigid intentions of Dr. Ramon.
Señor Acisclo's senior apprentice found that the new
boy was a scholar, and entrusted him with the delicate
business of writing his love letters to the maids and
seamstresses of Huesca. In return, he taught Santiago
to write lampoons about the monarchist burghers, and to
play on the guitar. It was not a bad life after all, this
being a barber's apprentice, and whenever he was
released from work, he had leisure to practise, not only
upon the guitar, but with his old instrument, the sling.

He could put a stone clean through a hat thrown up at
twenty yards. His rate of discharge was five to his
opponent's one. Being quite fascinated with the sling
and its uses, he even wrote out a little essay called
Lapidary Strategy, which, like another early work by
James Joyce was issued to the world in a private manu-
script edition of one copy. Santiago threw his soul into
each stone that came from his sling, and his head was
covered with scars where the enemies' fusillade had left
its mark. Santiago's skill and leadership made him once
again the undisputed captain of a band of boys and more
of a town nuisance than ever. These lads of Huesca
called themselves Monarchists and Democrats, and a
group of them were capable of routing a whole band of
Civil Guards. In such warfare, naturally, one had to be
ready for an occasional mishap. Santiago was once
captured by an enraged peasant who had been hit by a
stone catapulted from behind a wall, and despite his cries
that another boy had really fired the shot, received a
sound cudgelling. When at last the man let him go,
Santiago slipped again behind the wall and took his

stance lower down the road where presently his castiga-tor passed by, driving his mules and pleased to have taught that young devil a lesson. A dozen pebbles whizzed around his head, followed by larger stones that made the animals take fright and disperse. Seeing his mules scatter over the countryside, the peasant could do nothing but curse, and when eventually he reached the town went straight to the police. Unfortunately for justice, he could not remember in the least what that boy was like, and once more Santiago Ramon escaped. But others in Huesca remembered his face.

To the girls especially he had become an unholy terror. Whenever they saw that young bandit Santiago Ramon, they scattered as quickly as the mules. He was not yet interested in girls, but once, his glance did stray from his leather sling for long enough just to look at them, and pay notice to one timid little creature who lived in the *Calle del Hospital*. His glance made a complete and detailed portrait of her. Her large eyes were the shade of the green sea, over her little shoulders fell long straw-coloured plaits, and whenever she looked in his direction those cheeks became as red as geraniums. He realized that her fright was really a tribute to him-self. That pretty image of alarmed girlhood became fixed deeply in his fancy. One day later on, the picture was to be painted in even richer colours.

CHAPTER XII

AT THE SHOEMAKER'S

IT is not unexpected that a barber's apprentice who passed his spare time practising with the sling should reveal small aptitude for lessons, though the deficiency was less to his discredit than to the methods of teaching. Give him a pencil, and he could expose an idea. Let him do something with his hands, and he showed efficiency and neatness. But literary culture, grammar and catechism made fruitless appeal to faculties in Santiago that were not yet aroused because no schoolmaster ever inspired them. Dr. Ramon was disappointed. He had a further spasm of fear for the future. He himself was going through a bad time on account of a dispute with the Mayor of Ayerbe, and had decided to quit the town. For two years, the family lived in one of the outlying villages while the doctor kept up his implacable feud. Personal worries brought back his old dread of poverty, and he looked round for another opening to safeguard his boy's future, for to him it was clearer than ever that Santiago had no gifts for becoming a surgeon. This time, he apprenticed his boy to a shoemaker.

Unlike the spirited Señor Acisclo, the new master was an ill-favoured, brutal creature. Once more the boy learned the misery of wretched food; he slept in a garret with mice running about the straw and was not even able to practise drawing. He had only one resource, his vivid pictorial imagination. He would lie awake for hours staring at the stains and cobwebs on the walls,

transforming them into shapes that moved in a caval-
cade across a magic stage. Yet sometimes, even in that
rough life at the cobbler's bench, there were romantic
glimpses of a different world. A young Countess met
with an accident to her boot while hunting, and the
apprentice was allowed the felicity of taking into his
hands that elegant foot, to repair the doeskin. As he
glanced up into her eyes, he had a glimpse into that
legendary world where luxurious equipages followed the
huntsmen pursuing boars through the forest to the sound
of horns. When the repair was done to her boot, the
divine creature gave him a handsome tip. Once more
he could buy pencils and paper to beguile his loneliness.

We might pity Santiago Ramon, as one of Hans
Andersen's unhappy children, but that would be incor-
rect. He suffered passionate depressions, but the needle
of his compass always came back to his native hopeful-
ness. He was never morbid, never mistrusted the world
for long. Presently he was transferred to another master
who, at a hint from Dr. Ramon, fed him on vegetable
stew as though he had been a fractious mule. Santiago's
stomach was endowed with an unusual degree of Spanish
pride, and with his usual resourcefulness, he managed to
slip those offensive victuals into a handkerchief hidden in
his trouser pocket. His mother, well aware of her
husband's little ways, sent him supplies of food secretly.

Those months at the shoemaker's were not entirely
wasted. We can imagine the stern arguments that Don
Justo used about the necessity for learning life in a hard
school and the practical value of being taught to handle
first the razor, and now the needle. Once more, we may
allow him some small credit. Perhaps he was thinking
that the mastery of these implements would be useful in

a surgeon's career. Stronger, probably, than any ulterior educational purpose, was his fantastic fear of having a son unable to earn a living. That dual apprenticeship seemed a guarantee that Santiago would at least have a trade in his fingers, perhaps two. Craftsmanship in the making of an open-work toe and the graceful sheath for a feminine calf made an artistic appeal to Santiago.

Ramon y Cajal's greatness grew out of qualities his father neither perceived nor encouraged. In a sense, nothing he could do would really have hindered his son. Don Justo's role in his training was mainly that of a grindstone to a sensitive edge. His contribution lay in the power of opposition which developed Santiago's instincts into faculties. From adversity, this boy drew the force that made him stronger.

Such is the only explanation that bridges the paradox between the harsh methods of the father and the brilliant success of the son. When it has talent for raw material, opposition is a good means of training, although such a theory takes us back to the nineteenth century. Those Victorian heroes we read of, who educated themselves despite their small opportunities — boys like David Livingstone who studied a Latin grammar whilst working at a cottom loom — were at least fortunate in that they faced the world with an undivided will. Santiago Ramon was like that. They were not handicapped by the neurotic inhibitions which harass some modern boys.

CHAPTER XIII

A CARICATURE OF LEARNING

IN Don Justo's educational programme, two opposites struggled for mastery; yet to the pupil each equally uncongenial. The Latin grammar that Fray Jacinto had failed to drive into Santiago was balanced by the crude craftsmanship of barbering and shoemaking. Between these inflexible poles of discipline the boy struggled to follow the one pursuit in which he was genuinely interested — drawing and painting. Then came the moment when the father relented. He decided to remove his son from the shoemaker's workshop and send him back to school, much pleased with his own tolerance. At once he was faced with the old demand from Santiago: might he now have drawing lessons? The boy's increasing success in the art of parent-management was due to his clever exploitation of the fact that his father was so logical that he could only think of one objective at a time, and was prone to be defeated by surprise. Against this sudden repetition of an old idea, he could find no arguments, and a drawing teacher was engaged. Impressed with Santiago's talent, he innocently remarked that the boy should take up painting as well. At once Don Justo became suspicious again. That was going too far. His limited mental elasticity had been stretched enough. 'Painting? All I agreed to was drawing!' we can hear him say, defensively.

In the perpetual unexpectedness of life, once an object is attained, it has become already a past event.

Now he had reached one goal, another rose immediately before the ardour of boyhood. His progress so far had been chiefly in the sensory world of eye and hand. Now, the universe of intellect abruptly opened. He who had been so bad at lessons because he could never think except when he was making something, learned that he possessed a new power, that of reason.

Don Vicente Ventura, teacher of philosophy at the Institute, was the sort of schoolmaster who makes an impression. No boy at Huesca could fail to be dominated by his beak of a nose, his one blind eye covered with a shade, and his cataract of words. They whispered about his awe-inspiring character; for this man was a religious zealot accustomed to prostrate himself for hours at a time on the stone floor of the Cathedral, his arms spread out to resemble the Passion. They were fascinated by his discourses upon the doctors of the Church, especially Saint Thomas Aquinas, and his reverential attitude to scholastic philosophy. Don Vicente waxed hot as he denounced the wickedness of Rationalism and Liberalism. Any theory which remotely resembled individual judgment, which set itself against the authority of the Church, caused the classroom to echo with rhetorical thunder.

Most boys were bemused by this noisy eloquence upon themes far above their heads. They either accepted everything, or went to sleep; but in Santiago Ramon, the harangues of the teacher provoked a characteristic opposition. The man's vehemence roused his interest in abstract speculation, which grew into scepticism. The attraction to what was presented as dangerous led him to read writers like Voltaire. Don Vicente had done what no schoolmaster had ever done before. Santiago had grasped what it means to cogitate, and was led on to the exciting possibility that by the use of reason, one might discover the strongest possible position from which to attack authority. Don Vicente Ventura's orthodoxy helped to form one of the most liberal minds in Spain, though, it was to wear a protective caution that allowed him to dwell peacefully in a land of faith.

There was one final explosion, which tells us much about this phase of his development, which brings to a close his schooldays. His encounter with orthodoxy had a ludicrous ending.

Those lessons in drawing had liberated energy for mental exploration, yet he was still the adolescent Santiago Ramon, the individualist, to whom a virgin expanse of white was as irresistible a lure as a peach in a walled garden, or a policeman's cap as the target for a well-aimed stone. One day, going home from school, his head full of Don Vicente's fuming, he saw an empty wall and fell into temptation. With an ever ready stick of charcoal, he produced a sketch of a man's head, lifesize and lifelike, with a large nose and an unmistakable blind eye. The boys gathered around shouting: 'Look at the teacher, look at the one-eyed Don Vicente', and to express their sentiments, they pelted it with stones. Fate gave the final dramatic touch to the scene when Ventura appeared, and his single eye rested upon that apparition and on Santiago.

This lover of philosophy was by no means a mature human being. Those abasements on the Cathedral floor had not taught him tolerance. Even a night's reflection upon that horrible caricature brought no saving grace of humour, and next day in school, instead of attacking Voltaire, he let an avalanche of furious

egotism fall upon Santiago, and would not listen to the
boy's defence that he had meant the drawing as hero-
worship. Don Vicente was not even pacified when Dr.
Ramon, who was a personal friend, tried to soothe him
with an apology. How much the father regretted those
drawing lessons.

The end-of-term examinations at the Huesca Institute
were held in public, in the form of question and answer.
At the start of the proceedings, Don Vicente rose to his
feet and in a speech of rankling bitterness let go another
furious denunciation of that ungovernable pupil, who
had so wickedly exposed his master's effigy to the indig-
nity of being stoned in the streets. Pompously, he
declared before the whole school, conscience would not
allow him to take part in examining such a fellow.

The examiners did not behave as though they thought
their colleague mad. In the 1860s, it was the privilege
of a teacher to be always in the right. Santiago faced
their inquisitorial looks with the courage of despair and
a certain readiness of tongue. He pleaded that he had
worked hard in the last few months, but in view of Don
Vicente's words he would withdraw from the examination. As well might one accused before Torquemada try
to escape his fate. The examiners replied that they were
entirely above prejudice, in fact, were completely
impartial. He might submit himself confidently to their
sense of justice. Then they put him through the rack and
thumbscrew of philosophical dialectic, turned all his
answers against him, and after half an hour, let him creep
from the room, crushed with shame. He decided to run
away from home.

When Santiago Ramon announced a plan, others
were always ready to follow. A group of rebels set out for

open country, resolved to tramp as far as they could manage each day, sleeping in the mountains, getting their daily bread by begging and theft. They set out in a mood of high adventure. The first evening they reached a village where one of them had a schoolmaster uncle, and with the delightful irresponsibility that overtakes boys, they did not see any inconsistency in accepting supper and beds. These rebels against society had a jolly time dancing in the village square. After a good night's rest, the rebellion was called off. They walked back home to Huesca.

This was almost the last of his adventures of immaturity. Santiago Ramon had grown up slowly, had suffered much, but he bore no resentment. When he came to describe those early years, with the rueful amusement of an old man puzzled by the wild and foolish boy he had been, there was no revengeful desire for compensation. Those tribulations had left no mark upon Ramon y Cajal, who kept, until he was old, the charming elasticity of boyhood and a romantic faith in the Crusoe island.

CHAPTER XIV

BROMIDE AND BONES

AT last (and how relieved we are to hear it) Santiago Ramon managed to pass the leaving examination, and his schooldays at Huesca Institute came to an end. He was still immature, no more than a country boy, hesitating and rustic in speech. Owing to those mishaps with authority, and the interruption caused by the apprenticeship, he was behind others who had started level and were now out in the world. Santiago had little notion of what to do with his life. He passively adopted his father's plan of training to be a *Galenista*, a doctor. Ramon y Cajal should be the patron of late beginners. Even now he had only raw abilities, and no strong ambitions. We have to slow down our impatience to the tempo of his leisurely development, and observe the scientist grow from a gawky boy in surroundings where science had no existence. In the twilight period before he became a medical student, there are however two prophetic episodes.

In the crypt of the ruined church of St. Teresa, some Daguerrotypists had their almost secret laboratory, and a friend showed Santiago a marvel. There, in the glow of the red lamp was the metal plate, wet and glistening. On its dull surface was a thin coating of jelly containing bromide of silver. This plate, he was told, had been 'exposed' to light in the 'camera' behind the lens which was trained upon one of the young ladies of Huesca. Now in the darkness, the plate was dipped in the solution, and slowly before his eyes took place a miraculous transformation. On its dull surface, the features of the Señorita — her very expression, even her comb and mantilla became as sharp and clear as a drawing. When the plate was finished, he saw a portrait of such exquisite fidelity as he had never imagined. Details of her face and clothes had been captured by sunlight, chemically imprisoned in that film of collodion; then the developing process had set them free and produced the portrait of a living girl in all its depths and shades.

Such a description of the marvel of the year 1868 has today the flavour of a commonplace. We forget there was a time when photography was an art as much as a science, and it is hard to recapture the excitement of a country boy seeing it for the first time, the darkness of the crypt and the charm of the girl's face giving an added sense of mystery. Already photography had been more than half a century in growing, and the process which Santiago Ramon saw in use was probably the comparatively advanced technique of wet collodion. As a means of reproducing a faithful picture, this now discarded method has never been surpassed.

The effect on Santiago's mind was overwhelming. This union of art and craft aroused all his sensibilities. The things we do best are those we begin early. That chemical reaction between the silver salt and the developer became the germ of Ramon y Cajal's later scientific technique. He had hardly time to absorb this discovery, when Don Justo had another of his educational intuitions.

To Dr. Ramon, the most illustrious person in the fraternity of doctors was the surgeon, not the physician. The surgeon was the Napoleon of healing, the man who dominated and controlled. The physician might look imposing, in his scarlet robe and gold-tipped stick; but he could do no more than use herbs and incantations, and in his art there was too much of the magical to satisfy Don Justo's rational ideas. But surgical operations formed the spectacular side of a healer's destiny. Ordinary folk bowed before his crimson glory, a little blood heightening the splendour of success, giving it the hall-mark of popularity. He was never tired of lecturing his son upon this glorious vocation, and the basic fact that to be a surgeon, one had to have in one's fingers the details of human anatomy. In turn, the foundation of anatomy was the study of the bones. It was necessary to have specimens, and Don Justo fell back upon the homely method of self-help. To find the bones, father and son hit upon a manœuvre characteristic of both.

On a moonlit night they entered the churchyard. Santiago was adept at scaling walls, and the co-operation of his father made this nocturnal adventure quite respectable, though discovery would have been awkward. This time, father and son were wholly united, both in the pursuit and the secrecy. In one corner, half covered with stones and nettles, there was a pile of bones. After rummaging around this abundant charnel house they were able to make up a complete human skeleton. The boy thought more highly of anatomy on account of the adventure of gathering its raw materials. Femurs, vertebrae, and skulls passed between them, and Santiago's fingers explored every surface, every protuberance. He picked up anatomy quickly, and Don Justo was agreeably surprised; his son's supposedly bad memory then, was all nonsense. The truth was that he always found it easy to acquire knowledge through eyes and fingers, his being mainly a visual and tactile type of mind. The unconventional procedure of getting specimens by a ladder over a graveyard wall touched his imagination. Don Justo had at last found both the right subject and the right method. He began to reverse his previous opinions of Santiago's stupidity. Perhaps after all, his boy had the makings of a surgeon, and Don Justo optimistically planned a family migration to the old University city of Zaragoza where their partnership in anatomy would be continued under more favourable conditions.

CHAPTER XV

HERCULES AND VENUS

IN those last schooldays when his mind was full of the excitement of going to College, Santiago fell in love. She was a friend of his sisters, and as the girls sat around the fire talking and sewing, he would stare at them, in passionate silence. He never ceased to dream of her by day and night, yet he could not bring himself to say a single thing. Common words would have been too crude for the delicacy of his feelings. Though she was only fourteen, and he had said nothing, he was furiously jealous if he saw her going out with another boy. We can think of Santiago at the age of sixteen, walking alone in the long Spanish night, and envying those wooers in heavy cloaks each whispering to a face and a pair of eyes. He burned and smouldered, nursing his unexpressed feelings. All he ever did was to make drawings to offer her. When the girl's name was mentioned, Santiago became touchy and possessive. But that was all. Some more confident young man came along and was betrothed to her. We are happy for Santiago that his last days at Ayerbe, where he had suffered so much, were to be remembered for his first love.

Dr. Ramon first arranged for his son to become a temporary boarder in the house of a surgeon at Zaragoza. Then he went back the fifty miles to Ayerbe to make arrangements for giving up his practice, for he intended to restrict himself to anatomy. Presently he found an appointment in a Poor Law Clinic at Zaragoza, and this left him enough free time to carry on practical dissection in company with Santiago. They had now the privilege of actual dead bodies. No more stolen bones. The middle-aged doctor and his boy of seventeen were two zealots among the careless throng of students. Following a textbook written in French, they made a number of infinitely handsome preparations, sparing no time or effort to trace nerves and arteries to their terminations that were as delicate as fine hairs. To this joint work, the father brought his passionate belief, that was almost a religious faith.

Anatomical specimens are prone to decay, so that material upon which so much labour has been spent has to be thrown away. The boy began to sketch those evanescent appearances. Using his pencil and crayons he displayed muscles, arteries and nerves with convincing exactitude. His pictures were much better than those plain woodcuts in the French textbook. Don Justo felt a new emotion. On a matter which touched his sympathies, he was a clear-headed man, and now he perceived that the boy's despised talent could be of practical use. He who had been so blindly severe over that picture of the Apostle Saint James, and so credulous of the opinion of the town plasterer, was now delighted. He felt he had sired a genuine anatomist. This boy's gift could lead to fame. Together, they would compose a wonderful new textbook, for which Santiago would provide the illustrations. It would be used everywhere in Spanish-speaking countries.

As for Santiago, he began to live another of his lives. His father, pleased by his assiduity in the anatomy room, allowed him leisure to explore this capital of Aragon, where two hundred years before the great Velazquez had painted the broken bridge spanning the Ebro.

The seventeenth-century Cathedral possessed a sacred pillar on the top of which Our Lady had appeared to Saint James the patron of Spain, only forty years after the death of Christ. In keeping with such venerable tradition, the scientific teaching in the Medical Faculty was weak. There were numerous lectures, but no laboratories. Although the period of Santiago's medical study happened to coincide with seven years of comparative political freedom, between the death of the Bourbon Queen Isabella II and the accession of Alfonso XII, the spirit of Liberalism had not reached the Medical Faculty. Freemasonry was apt to be confused with Darwinism as a dangerous heresy. Europe was beginning to study bacteria. But in Zaragoza perhaps the modern spirit was best exemplified in the labours of that assiduous father and son who pursued their filigree of dissection.

It is unlikely that Santiago worked quite as hard as his father, but he knew how to use what he knew. The Professor of Midwifery inquired why Señor Ramon was present so seldom at his lectures. He received the lofty answer that Señor Ramon, though occupied with anatomy, had nevertheless bestowed some attention on midwifery, and thought himself well prepared. The Professor thereupon asked him a complicated question about the development of the embryo, a specialized point upon which the average student would be weak. For Santiago, it was a lucky hit. In this field the two Ramons were as well informed as anyone in Zaragoza. Seizing coloured chalks, he gave his answer in half an hour's demonstration on the blackboard. The students applauded, and the Professor, though he must have suspected a lamentable ignorance in other directions, had for good form's sake to say that in future Señor Ramon might attend lectures as seldom as he pleased. It was another case of Santiago's resourcefulness in escape. Besides anatomy, he had other interests in life.

A fellow student had beaten him in a wrestling match, and Santiago who was as vain of his muscles as of his drawing, remembered a similar rebuff when he was a new boy at Huesca. He recalled too the revenge which had been possible through physical training. He found a gymnastic teacher, and made a bargain that they would exchange lessons — Santiago teaching physiology in return for advice upon muscular development. He possessed an ability much more efficacious than any system — his power of concentration: in everything, he overvalued, did more than was strictly necessary. Each day he practised balancing, jumping and throwing heavy balls. He was never seen strutting along the *Alameda* without a large umbrella, which he swung aggressively. It was in fact an iron bar, weighing sixteen pounds, and painted in neat folds. Anyone who had the misfortune to shake hands received the crushing grip of an athlete's paw. In the year when his beard began to grow, he became a tiresome Hercules with bulging pectorals and iron biceps, contemptuous of all professors and students. As he strutted along, he would cast up his eyes to the balconies of the houses, and one day, he saw his Venus. She had large blue eyes and gave him a sunny smile. Santiago soon got to know her name, and even to possess her photograph. Direct approach was of course unthinkable, but once, during the carnival when both wore masks, he managed to whisper a few words in her ear, though she did not know him for the young man who passed her window swinging that formidable umbrella.

There was a second admirer, a student of engineering, who also gazed up at the same eyes in the same balcony. Presently, the two young men came face to face. The girl would have been entertained to hear what passed between them. The engineer arrogantly forbade Ramon ever to pass that way again, on pain of a tremendous beating. He cannot have suspected what lay beneath the neat folds of that umbrella. Ramon issued his challenge to fight, and they adjourned to a wood, each provided with a stout cudgel. On the way to the duelling ground, they relieved their feelings with ponderous ironies.

'It is a pity, Señor Ramon, that you are so far advanced with your university course, since those years of study will be wasted, now that your honour's days are numbered.'

'In your own case, Señor, the loss will not be so great, since you are, if I am not mistaken, only in your first year.'

Neither of them lost face, and Santiago contemptuously invited the other to begin. Three resounding thwacks on his skull was the answer he received. Then with precipitous attack, he leapt upon the engineer, seized him by the shoulders, whirled him three times round in the air and left him unconscious on the ground. After this, the spirit of chivalry took control. Their mood became one of great friendliness, and the engineer admitted he was beaten. Santiago could not wear his hat because of the three great lumps on his head. In their new spirit of tolerant understanding they decided that the honourable line of action was for each of them to write a letter, begging the girl to be graciously pleased to make a choice between her two humble admirers after this reconciliation. They parted, shaking hands. Next day, the engineer came to Ramon in great distress. He had found out one important fact that rendered it dishonourable for either of them to make a proposal. It turned out that the lady was an heiress. How could two impecunious students think of offering themselves? As a man of punctilio, Santiago Ramon agreed that it was unthinkable.

Their rivalry had come to an abrupt end, before either of them had said one word to the girl. The boys remained friends — but she, the object of this passion, had another fate. Later on Santiago heard that she had died of tuberculosis, quite unaware of their distant and unexpressed admiration.

Santiago Ramon had many other adventures, romantic and intellectual, before he qualified as a doctor at the age of twenty-one. He tried his hand at many things, with prodigious but fitful zeal. One week, he would spend every day in the library reading philosophy. Then he would work himself to a standstill in the dissecting room. His faculties were growing, in every direction, but unevenly, one castle of ability stood beside a small cottage, and his lack of all sense of time or continuity was always leading him into ludicrous situations. Once he turned up to a written examination a whole hour late, was admitted only after fierce entreaties, and by the time he had answered the first question — on cholera — he had to give in his paper.

He was still under his father's influence, and had not acquired an independent personality. At last, in the year 1873, he took his diploma, and jumped at the chance of going into the army. This for Santiago was an opportunity for travel and romance.

CHAPTER XVI

LIFE IN THE ARMY

OUT of a hundred candidates examined for the Army Medical Corps, he passed in sixth and was able to sport his uniform before his friends in Zaragoza on his way to join his unit campaigning in the north. In 1873 Don Carlos was making one of his futile attempts on the crown of Spain. He had been defeated at Oroquista, but being a Spaniard, did not know the meaning of compromise, and the civil war dragged on in Catalonia. It was old-fashioned campaigning, carried out at the speed of the horse, and quite lacking the ruthlessness of modern warfare. The Royal troops would surround a village, then find the rebels had disappeared. In eight months of evasive manœuvring over the torrid plateau of Spain, Lieutenant Ramon never treated a single wound. But he was enjoying himself greatly. Though a doctor was entitled to be mounted, he generally preferred to go on foot. Two orderlies were on hand to spy out choice provisions, and save him the bother of collecting his pay from the quartermaster. The military terrain of that war was his ancestral Aragon and Catalonia, where the peasants welcomed anyone who was a native. Often when quartered in a town, it would be hard to tear himself away from a round of banquets and flirtations. He once even penetrated through the Carlist lines, disguised as a peasant, and was able to pay a surreptitious visit to his parents in Zaragoza.

How impatiently Don Justo regretted this army phase. He was longing for Santiago to begin that professional career that would make him a professor. The father felt that his long struggle against the boy's shortcomings was over, and on the whole, he was not displeased with the result. Then like a thunderbolt came paralysing news. Santiago had actually volunteered to serve in Cuba.

Cuba! The boy must be insane. Cuba, that grave of Spaniards, that pestilent hole of yellow fever, malaria, the most unhealthy spot in the Western hemisphere. Dr. Ramon fell back into his old despair. Was it for this he had made all his sacrifices?

The West Indian colonists had taken advantage of the disordered state of the Spanish homeland to begin a guerrilla rebellion in the forests and swamps, and were slowly wearing down the strength of the Spanish expeditionary forces. Compared to the dry and healthy life in the army at home, service in Cuba was deadly. But for Santiago Ramon it was a chance to find his Crusoe island, to follow the great Christopher Columbus into a new world. He was now hardened against the rage of his father. He was free, and decided for himself.

Don Justo wrote bitterly reproaching his son, and threatening death, chronic illness and every conceivable horror. And when that failed, he wrote to anyone who might have influence, begging that his brilliant boy might be given a post in a base hospital.

At this moment the father had another cause for anxiety. Just when he was distracted at losing his eldest in the dangers of the Caribbean, his second boy, the dutiful Pedro, showed up in his true colours. He who had been a model of good behaviour had actually run away to South America and disappeared, leaving no trace. Don Justo felt he had never understood either of his boys. The obedience of Pedro was worse even than the wilfulness of Santiago. Both of them had acquired somewhere — it was not from him — a streak of madness which contradicted all his cautious Catalan instincts.

It was no use. Santiago was delighted to be leaving and wearing, with a peaked *képi*, an elegant suit of white with three stars on his sleeve and a broad double stripe of gold down to his ankles, he embarked at the port of Cadiz, where for two centuries the inhabitants had guarded the gate to the Indies, and made every traveller their perquisite and their prey. Urchins demanded extortionate tips, every article in the shops cost double; Santiago was relieved to be at last in a rowing boat making for the ship anchored outside. Then as they were clear of the harbour, the boatman put down his oars, complained of a strong westerly wind, and demanded twice the fare. But he was not dealing with an easy going Andalusian or a soft gentleman from Madrid. This tough youth from Navarre was out of humour with the people from Cadiz. The athlete of Zaragoza leapt forward and took the boatman by the throat, actually threatened to break his neck. The west wind immediately abated, and the oars were resumed quickly. Evidently, this young officer was a man from the north. He lacked a sense of decorum.

Santiago Ramon — born in the mountains — was thrilled to be for the first time in his life on the water. Over his head the great Tropic Constellation branched and twinkled, and below, the dark sea was alive with phosphorescence. Every seagull, each movement of the porpoises in the water, was romance. It was eighteen days before they anchored beneath the white fortress of Habana, and he saw his first tropical town, which had been built by the followers of the great Columbus.

CHAPTER XVII

A BEAUTIFUL VIEW

HIS first impression was of being among his own people, yet transported back to the golden age when Spain had ruled most of the world. Around him those partly Hispanic mulattoes spoke a charming dialect of Andalusian. His Crusoe island had a belt of green stretching up the sides of the hills from the white houses. Santiago demanded to be taken to the tropical forest. Vaguely, his guide pointed to a straggling thicket. Disappointment came over Santiago Ramon. True, there were bananas with great sabre shaped leaves and scarlet flowers, there were Royal palms thirty feet high, and oak trees hung with beards of moss, yet — this forest lacked dignity, and the birds were hardly any bigger than those at home. He had expected jaguars and rattle-snakes.

A proper use of Don Justo's letters of recommendation would have found him a safe post in a hospital in Habana where he could get others to do his routine work, leaving himself free for research and life in the cafés. But Santiago was not the person to play safe. He was determined to penetrate the real forest. He found that no difficulty whatever was placed in his path. Other officers, who had more discreetly used their own letters of introduction, were glad to make way for this simpleton, and after a complicated journey by boat and armoured railway train, he found himself at a military outpost in the wilds of Camaguay; it was named *Vista Hermosa*. As he looked at the thick green jungle all around him, he did not at first appreciate that this place might have been named 'beautiful view' with an ironic intention. He was supremely happy. At last, he had realized his romantic dream of being in a small island of civilization surrounded by the endless primitive life of the forest.

Spanish military strategy in Cuba was to parcel out this long attenuated island into fortified sections, which were connected by military roads guarded every few miles by blockhouses. But the Indian rebels passed through those barriers like air, and each Spanish reinforcement was very costly. From the wooden building that was his hospital, Ramon looked out each day on the dark green edge of the forest. It was impossible to venture there, or even set foot outside the enclosure where, separated only by a few planks from two hundred wretches lying ill with malaria and dysentery, he worked and slept in a cubicle, surrounded by bags of sugar and jars of drugs. In one corner, he set up a dark room for photography, and there was plenty of leisure for sketching in this wilderness. He began also to study the English language.

The deadliest enemies of the Spanish Colonial army were, of course, not the Cuban natives, but those diseases that harassed every European adventurer since Cortés and Pizarro. Yellow fever was more frequent than bullet wounds. Spanish soldiers in those sordid barracks had no defence against the clouds of gnats that came over from the forest at nightfall, bringing that malady characteristic of the New World, and to which the natives, infected for generations, had gradually become immune. A few kilometres away in Habana, a medical practitioner named Carlos Juan Finlay had a theory that yellow fever was conveyed by the bite of a mosquito. As yet, no one believed him; and as for malaria, — in these forest clearings it was so frequent as to be considered a normal part of life. Years were still to pass before a member of the Indian Medical Service, Ronald Ross, had the inspiration that traced this disease also to a mosquito and led to its control. Against both yellow fever and malaria a doctor's resources in 1874 were miserable. Lying in his cubicle reading a book, or finishing a sketch of the beautiful view, Santiago Ramon had only one remedy to treat the soldiers and safeguard himself — large doses of the drug which his forefathers named Jesuits' bark, and we call quinine. Even that was not sufficient to protect him. He was soon caught by malaria and had to drag himself through his daily round, harassed by attacks of shivering.

Then abruptly, the quietness, the suffocating calm of this idleness, would be invaded by gunfire. Feeling so sick with fever that he could hardly put on his boots, the doctor would get up, load his rifle, and take his stand at one of the windows. With a few shots, a quick movement at the edge of the forest, a stray bullet on the wooden walls — the futile eruption of a rebel attack had passed before the defenders knew what was happening. As a rule such sorties came to nothing, and Ramon might take off his boots and go back to his book. Yet the Spaniards at *Vista Hermosa* could never forget that on one occasion an entire garrison at another blockhouse had been wiped out by the natives.

By temperament, Santiago Ramon was unsuited to this useless inertia. His colleagues found relief in cards and endless gossip. They at least had no desire to do any more, and indolence was less of a strain. Ramon was a peasant from the north, and purposeful activity had

grown to be habit. Besides, politically, he was a man of
the Left, and on listening to the officers' talk, he was
amazed to hear pronounced monarchist opinions, Spain
being at that time a Republic. His political innocence
received a shock when that form of government came to
an end, and Alphonso XII was proclaimed King;—
Santiago had penetrated neither the mentality of his
brother officers, nor the outlook at home.

Some months at *Vista Hermosa*, turned him into an
emaciated, shivering, anaemic wreck, and he was posted
for duty to a base hospital at *Puerto Príncipe*, though he
was quite unfit for active work.

At the base, the officers led a more sociable existence,
mulatto women being there to beguile them, as well as
those other West Indian attractions, rum and limes. In
the cafés, the dominating grievance was that of soldiers'
pay. It was small enough, and worse, it was hardly ever
received. One senior officer had embezzled large funds
and escaped to the U.S.A.; but chronic maladministra-
tion was more serious than occasional fraud. All officers
lived upon credit with the local shops—all except
Lieutenant Ramon. He was frugal and he disliked
owing money. He made the truly Quixotic plan of paying
the stores and cafés by means of loans from other officers.
It seemed to him a more dignified method, but it failed
to please. It made an exceedingly bad impression. He
was a known Republican, and now he was proved to be
a man of peasant instincts who paid his debts. The army
authorities had their revenge upon this individualist.
Although still convalescent, he was posted to a wretched
hospital at a place called *San Isidro*, overlooking a swamp,
where unsatisfactory officers were sent to give them a
taste of discipline. Here, there were always more men

in hospital than on duty. It had not even the compensation of a beautiful view.

Santiago Ramon's radical views were aired freely at *San Isidro*. Spain, he told them vehemently, dreamed that it was still the world of Philip II; politicians in Madrid who had never set foot in Cuba, were saying that the colony must be defended to the last man and last peseta. England and Holland, he argued, managed to hold their Caribbean colonies, but Spain was losing her's. Around him in that miserable swamp he saw the reasons. That system of fortified blockhouses was making no impression at all upon the timeless Indians, who were never defeated because never engaged. Spain was behaving with her usual blind lack of adaptability, like the two Spaniards in the legend who fought for an apple and killed one another.

Ramon also poked his nose into details of hospital administration in a manner unpardonable in an officer. When 'light diet' was ordered, he found that the patients received only boiled out chicken, since the best portions had found their way into the officers' mess. The same was the case with eggs and wine. It was an old army custom, they told him, with a wave of the hand. 'What other way would you have, *Señor Teniente?*' Sergeants, Corporals, cooks were ready to point out to this rash Quixote that his giants were only windmills. But Ramon, shaking with malaria, bitter under the shame of this enterprise, insisted that rations should be fairly divided, and he exposed hospital abuses in detailed dispatches to the Army Commander.

Nevertheless, he was at the end of his tether. His tough mountain physique, in a sense, was against him in this jungle; for where a feebler organism would have succumbed, he continued, half exhausted. Six months at *San Isidro* almost killed him. At last, swallowing his pride, he applied for his discharge from the army on grounds of ill-health. Fortune helped him, as *San Isidro* was being abandoned. Ramon found himself a hospital patient and recommended for repatriation to Spain.

The grotesqueness of this Cuban adventure continued to the end. The doctor in charge of the hospital was a man of violent temper, whose self-control had been sapped by tuberculosis. When his orders were not obeyed promptly, he would fire off his revolver to gain attention. Even when fit to stand on his feet, Ramon could not leave Cuba because the army would not disgorge his arrears of pay, and he was obliged to write home to his father for money. Using this loan, he was able to stop in Habana long enough to achieve his only victory. The Paymaster smiled, evaded, smoked a cigar. Each day, Lieutenant Ramon appeared in his office, persistent, inflexible. At last, a bargain was struck as between *caballeros*. Arrears of pay were handed over, and Ramon gave his receipt in full for the money. What he actually counted was about sixty per cent of the sum mentioned in the papers. After all, the Paymaster himself was entitled to live; perhaps he too was awaiting the payment of arrears.

Robinson Crusoe returned from his island, a pale emaciated figure, richer only in experience, and in six hundred pesetas. That money he had wrested from the Paymaster was to found a great scientific career. For him, this colonial experience had been more fortunate than the affair had been for Spain. This little colonial war had cost 74,000 Spanish casualties, and achieved no more than a temporary pacification of Cuba.

CHAPTER XVIII

THE MICROSCOPE AND THE SILVER

DON JUSTO RAMON, on seeing the drawn face and yellowish pallor of his son, knew that his dark forebodings had been realized, all but the very darkest. His eldest boy was still alive; but not a single line had come from the inexplicable Pedro whose bones might be lying in some forest of South America. Santiago was convalescent but despondent. Don Justo, once more in a position of moral authority, insisted on the next objective — Santiago must go to Madrid to take the full medical qualification. Upon this, Don Justo was adamant, and on this occasion he was correct. Like many gifted youths who loathe discipline, Santiago might have been ready to go on with a dilettante existence, sketching, dissecting and photographing. But in his present state of weakness, he gave way to his father, realizing perhaps that to take his diploma might be his best chance to shake himself free.

All examinations have their secrets, quite apart from their subject matter. Instead of preparing himself in Zaragoza, Santiago would have been wiser to go up to Madrid a little in advance, to be coached in the idiosyncrasies of the examiners, some of whom favoured textbooks not generally used: while others expected candidates to know about their own professorial teaching even though this was unorthodox. Students in the capital were familiar with these points, but the young man up from Zaragoza had to cram new material into his head in a few nights, feverish study. The gods of the emergency were always kind to Ramon. His Socratic face must have inspired confidence. He was tactful, yet tenacious, and they let him pass.

That visit to Madrid led him to something much more significant than merely passing an examination. Only a few weeks before a friend in Zaragoza had let him look down the tube of a microscope, and he had seen the entrancing vision of blood cells, much magnified, actually alive and circulating in the blood vessels of a frog's webbed foot. Filled with excitement, he resolved to possess a microscope of his own. He happened to see in a shop window, an instrument of French make, and bought it; or rather he paid the first instalment, and took it home to Zaragoza. The full cost was the equivalent of a hundred pounds. He purchased also an instrument called a microtome, which cut tissues into thin shavings suitable for examination, and some French textbooks. His mastery of English, acquired at *Vista Hermosa*, was now good enough to encourage him to subscribe to the *Quarterly Journal of Microscopical Science*, edited in London by Professor Ray Lankaster.

The opening of an original career was thus due to malaria. Without that trying experience, Ramon would never have had leisure to learn English, or to save money. To go back further to the causes of things, his scientific work had really opened with the Crusoe romance that first led him to Cuba. He was to find in this new world which the microscope revealed a fascination, which had failed him in the forest of Camaguay. Yet had his father not insisted upon the examinations, there might have been no microscope. Each fortuitous circumstance appears a step in a predetermined purpose that now unfolds.

He was back in Zaragoza ready with his instruments. An innocent eye is the best teacher, and Ramon y Cajal's visual faculty was quite extraordinary. He was able to look at things with the primitive freshness of the first man; and what he saw was a new field, unmeasurable and unexplored. Some University teachers in Zaragoza had heard of the microscope. There were even examples of this marvel preserved in glass cases, but the professors hardly ever put their sceptical eyes to the lens. A Spaniard, says Ortega y Gasset, is apt to take an innovation as a personal affront. These men were indifferent to what might be found in the examination of properly prepared specimens. They preferred to imagine what was there, or to deduce it from a textbook which some French writer had developed from an Arabic translation of an idea which Galen had derived from Aristotle. The Spanish Inquisition had discouraged the idea of original investigation. In Zaragoza, Santiago Ramon was practically the only observer of this new microscopic field among intelligent men who were wilfully blind to it through neglect of an instrument they had never learned to use. Ramon might rage against their conservatism; yet how fortunate he was to be the lone worker in so rich a vineyard. His lifetime's harvest was to be nearly three hundred papers and fifteen textbooks.

He began to examine the simplest specimens, staining them according to the textbook, and making a careful sketch of each preparation.

Don Justo did not have much faith in the microscope, but he was glad to have Santiago under his eye at Zaragoza, to prepare him for the next step in the professional handicap. Professorships in the Spanish Universities were awarded by a quaint procedure of question and answer known as the *oposiciones* — the 'oppositions'. It was a contest of intellectual argument between the candidate and a board of professors who hear his thesis and then cross-examine him. The method was supposed to guarantee fairness and discourage favouritism. It derived, no doubt, from the theological procedure of the Middle Ages, when all questions were settled by logical debate between doctors of the canon law. Applied to the filling of medical professorships it was cumbersome, and had unsatisfactory results. The system was abandoned for a time when Catalonia became autonomous in 1931, but has since returned. Professor Gregorio Marañón of Madrid has described the *oposiciones* as 'the cancer and shame of Spanish Universities'.

At his first attempt, Ramon was unsuccessful. He was almost as much out of his element before these examiners as the schoolboy had been when accused by the infuriated Don Vicente. His way of speaking was still rustic. He was intelligent, but lacked polish. Other aspirants had practised the trick of embroidering their arguments with quotations, but Ramon used the dry and realistic approach he had learned from Don Justo. Chairs were going in Zaragoza and Granada, but he obtained neither. The members of the tribunal preferred more showy candidates, and Santiago Ramon was told to go home, improve his style, and try again. He managed no doubt through his father's influence to get a minor post in the Anatomical Museum at Zaragoza. Eight years were to pass before he reached the professorship which Don Justo so ardently desired.

Waiting for dead men's chairs is frustration to youth; and the mental struggle continued with his father, yet apart from those antagonisms inevitable between two of

Ramon blood, the pair of them were much alike. Despite disagreement, there was between them none of the bitter hatred such as Samuel Butler had for his father about the same period; nor the lack of intellectual sympathy which Edmund Gosse describes in *Father and Son*. Below the surface, Don Justo and his son were two bits of Aragon granite, of similar texture. Allowed to work at his microscope, Santiago could bear the gloomy moralizing of his father over the folly of the Cuban enterprise. The boy was kept working as though he were still a schoolboy. But medical schools in Spain were few, and professors tenacious of life. These were years of the hardest labour and disappointment.

In one vital respect, Santiago was outside his father's comprehension— in those artistic sympathies he was now able to develop. In complicated drawings, he was able to present an original view of some animal tissue, and when it was illustrated, its essential novelty was plain to others. He began to be sure he was on the right road. At this point, fate began to be angry with his persistence, and used her well-known power of curbing this rash adventurer, who presumed to probe so deeply into the mysteries of nature.

One evening, in the garden of the *Café Iberia*, Santiago was playing chess. This game aroused his pugnacity. He was out to checkmate his opponent, and there was no half-heartedness in his determination. Suddenly, he coughed, put his handkerchief to his mouth. There, quite unmistakable, was the red stain of fresh blood. Later that evening, he had a second haemorrhage, a frothy, copious stream from the lungs, filling his mind with irresistible dread. When Don Justo came to prescribe, it was only too clear from his face that father and son had reached the same diagnosis.

It was obvious, of course — once it had happened. Ever since his return from Cuba, the boy had been wretchedly pale and thin. Like others and Santiago himself, the doctor father had mistakenly put this down to malaria. Yet what had occurred, was staring them in the face. In those years — it was now only too clear — tuberculosis, even more insidious than malaria, had been making headway. At the end of the nineteenth century, that word tuberculosis meant a death sentence which would be executed without respite, after some months of depressing invalidism. Santiago had a cough, and was short of breath, and for the first time in his life, his courage wavered. This suspense was worse even than lying on a bunk in the blockhouse at *Vista Hermosa* waiting for Indians to burst out of the forest. His optimism had always been extravagant: now, his misery was extravagant too.

In the months of acute illness, while his temperature bounded up and down with his fears, an intense, morbid insight made him see the whole of his life like a picture, painted in tragic colours. Bitterly he reproached himself for squandering that capital of good health which his peasant forebears had left him. He tormented himself with the prospect of death and eternal punishment. Then, across the picture a ray of light would fall; but it was only enjoyment of his misery, a philosophic pessimism that wrung perverse pleasure out of the thought of submission to destiny. Again the colours changed, became hectic with protest and rebellion, as he demanded from life its fullest length and its promised satisfactions.

When the acute fever died down, and Don Justo thought it safe for him to leave his bed, Santiago was packed off to Panticosa, a mineral spa in upper Aragon, where he could take the waters, under the care of his sister Paula. They stayed in a half-ruined convent high up among pine trees. Here the sky was so blue as to seem black. In that limitless expanse he found peace and the promise of health: then his pessimism would return, like those dark valleys and craggy mountainsides where vultures lived.

Santiago ignored doctors' orders, and followed his own whims. Paula could not restrain him. He walked and walked, devouring the country with his eyes. When he should have rested, he took exercise. Even for the year 1876 it was an unconventional way to treat tuberculosis. By coincidence, in the Adirondack mountains of North America, another consumptive member of the medical profession was doing the same thing. He was Edward Livingstone Trudeau who, turning his back on hospitals, had gone to live in the inaccessible mountain wilderness. His prospect of life was so brief that his friends allowed him to enjoy that extraordinary regime. It needed two such winters for Dr. Trudeau to cure himself, and he lived forty years longer. Santiago Ramon was possessed of an even more exuberant vitality.

He talked with other tuberculous invalids at Panticosa, but their irrational optimism made him so contemptuous of medical knowledge, that he gave up drinking the Spa waters altogether. Reading the Italian poet Giacomo Leopardi taught him to feed upon his own melancholy, as though it were a positive force. Yet pessimism tended towards destruction. One autumn day, he climbed the highest hill and faced the snowcrests of the Pyrenees. He saw that range of mountains which as a despondent schoolboy at Jaca he had longed to conquer. Now the same impulse entered his head but with a different intensity. He would walk on and on, challenging nature to take him into her eternal winter. He would tramp far from men with no witness but eagles, no other shroud than the snows of autumn.

In that moment of crisis, he discovered something new — about himself and the universe. He found that there is a limit to human will power; man cannot use it to end his life, for will power implies life. However great his despair and the magnetism of death, he could not force himself into the arms of annihilation. Nature had thrown back his challenge. Back home to Panticosa he walked, feeling much better!

As he accepted that decisive realization, the visible world began to draw him away from his gloom. The beauty and splendour of the world made him resolve to live. He took out his camera once more. Here he was in beautiful Aragon, and he could visit the tombs of the ancient kings who had ruled this land before Spain even came to be.

Those few months in Panticosa restored the balance of his emotions. Returning to Zaragoza, greatly improved, he realized how much he owed to photography. His pictures were greatly admired, especially his tableau of the Provincial Governor in his box at the bullfight, surrounded by ladies in mantillas and high combs. Not merely was artistic flair shown in the composition of these pictures: his actual technique much developed when he learned to use a gelatine emulsion which had replaced the old collodion. Its perfection and simplicity made him think of going in for the manufacture of photographic materials on a large scale. In fact silver bromide had begun to exercise a decided influence in his life, and plans for exploiting its possibilities grew out of his pleasure in the mere handling of those plates. He felt the camera could accomplish more than the paintbrush. His father's old opposition had given him a sense of deficiency in his own gift for painting. His divided will toward this talent led him to unify drawing and photography into one original objective.

That previous plan of his father to publish their textbook of anatomy had never matured because the printers of Zaragoza were unequal to the task. Likewise the manufacture of photographic materials came to nothing. It was well that Santiago never went into commerce, for his enterprises would have been likely to fail. Photography had helped him to recover from tuberculosis.

Now, at last, he was able to take the irrevocable step— away from philosophic pessimism, away from the unsatisfying past.

CHAPTER XIX

FOLLY AND HAPPINESS

S O marked was Santiago's capacity for landing himself into foolish situations, that Don Justo cannot have felt at all secure when his son returned from the spa of Panticosa. Against all medical expectation, he was cured of his tuberculosis; but there was no foreseeing the next manifestation of inner weakness. The boy had come home from Cuba a physical wreck; two or three attempts to rise into the ranks of University teaching had failed; his precarious health had given way, and at nearly the age of thirty, he was no more than a badly paid employee of the University. Dr. Ramon nursed the thought of his ambitions, and his sacrifices. Pedro was still swallowed up in South America, and even if he were alive, sent no news. Then the worst happened. The father was prepared for everything except this final folly. Santiago plunged into the imprudence of getting married.

She was indeed that same timid little girl who had run away in terror from the bandit Santiago Ramon. He remembered her cheeks like geraniums ever since those days, and the long plaits of flaxen hair. Her sea-green eyes, veiled by long lashes, gave melancholy to her madonna-like face, suggesting a picture by Raphael. She was a peasant girl, and an orphan, a blonde — like Marguerite in *Faust* — unlike the common Iberian type. They were married in private, almost in secret, for Santiago took care not to allow time for his family to disapprove. He was indeed in the toils of an exquisite madness, more deep and moving than anything before in his life. Don Justo met a will power stronger than his own, and he must have known this was the end of his reign over his son. He was not a far-seeing man, and did not suspect that marriage was to be not an end but a beginning.

Santiago's success and a lifetime of good health opened with his marriage which was supremely happy and conventional. The wife accepted his career and his ambitions, and though she was content to be housewife and mother, her influence was profound. In later years, Ramon y Cajal said that a man of culture would be lost in the blue unless the woman, like the ballast and cord of a balloon, prudently drew him back to earth. His wife fertilized his spirit, and pruned away the excesses of imagination, giving his roots a chance to strike deep.

In his views upon women he was himself, a Spaniard of tradition, an orthodox male of the Victorian age, to whom they were still soft creatures to be protected. She exercised in secret a wife's prodigious power, unobtrusive, yet unrelenting, because both knew it was to last for life. Yet outwardly, she seems to play no part. The first results of her influence were seen in the sudden burst of luck which declared that his apprenticeship was over.

In 1880, the first year of his marriage, he gathered the results of his labours with the microscope and published a careful study upon inflammation. There were two illustrations, drawn and lithographed by himself: a hundred copies were printed and presented to his friends and the great men of Zaragoza. Their reaction was urbane, and characteristic of Spanish science. They said: 'Does our Santiago Ramon have the audacity to set himself up against foreign authorities?' They scanned that native-born product, and dismissed it as a piece of bravura, reserving their deference for those august foreign publications which they had never read.

Inflammation is the process by which a tissue of the body resists attack — whether by injury or disease. Inflammation is the epic of the battles between the body cells and their invaders. No medical theme could be more primary. Ramon's method of study was to follow the process through microscope sections, in a way to be described later.

Now came a second prize from the Fortune which had begun to notice him. He was successful in the *oposiciones*, and in 1883 was appointed to a professorship in the University of Valencia, on the Mediterranean coast, at an annual salary of 3500 pesetas.

Valencia had been called the Athens of Spain, and the intellectual atmosphere of the south was more congenial than Zaragoza. This was not the austere arid north, but an Arcadia of tamarisks and lemons, oranges and palms, with the sea as a silver line in the distance. In contrast to the energy of Aragon and the business efficiency of Catalonia, everything in Valencia was ease and languor — that gentler rhythm of southern life which seems to move between *fiesta* and *siesta* — dangerous perhaps for a tough-fibred Aragonese who might be seduced by its charm, with loss of his desire to achieve. This delicate-looking professor of thirty with a swart beard, who said goodbye to the anatomy rooms at Zaragoza, had survived enough perils to make him immune to the subtle risks of ease. Instead of being softened, he was liberated.

Members of the Medical Faculty heard with astonishment but approval that he did not intend to enter medical practice or compete for the favours of the wealthy Valencians, but meant to follow a whole time scientific career. He set up a laboratory in a large spare room of his house in the *Calle de los Avellanos* — Chestnut Street, and settled to enjoy the excitement of his first home.

The smiling Mediterranean province of Valencia had been made rich by the Arabs. Their talent for irrigation had turned it into a veritable Mahomet's paradise, and each Thursday, as in the days of the Califs, in the *Puerta de los Apostales*, the tribunal controlling the water supply still held its sittings publicly, in the open air. Santiago Ramon had travelled a long way since he found Huesca a large city, but the fascination of the south took hold. Apart from his family, and a bout of chess in the café, he allowed nothing to distract him from the world of the microscope. He used his eyes with a single-hearted vision, prepared to behold marvels, and record them in the sober language of science. His chosen subject was outside the range of most members of the Faculty. It was *Histology* — a science which explores, at a level invisible to the naked eye, each portion of the body, and finds it a web woven by the fertile complexity of life.

CHAPTER XX

FIRST PUBLICATION

RAMON Y CAJAL used to say, with astringent jocularity, that he had chosen Histology for his life's work because it was cheap. To make important discoveries, one needed no more than a microscope and a few chemical stains — provided one also possessed the will power to use them. No complicated apparatus was required — merely patience, and the seeing eye. Histology was an extension of the anatomy his father taught. But Don Justo knew nothing of this new sort of anatomy devoted to the ultra-small. For him, what could be seen and explored with his scalpel was all the practising surgeon needed to know. This magnifying and probing beneath the surface seemed a waste of effort.

The relationship between the two — what the father taught and what the son explored — was the difference between geography and geology. Like a geographer who describes the countries of the world as they are seen from the outside, Don Justo the anatomist approached the bodily organs as they appear to the naked eye. But the geologist is not content with that superficial acquaintance. He takes a hammer and breaks off bits of rocks which he examines and from which he deduces the structure of the earth's crust that lies beneath. Likewise, the man who practises histology, is not content to know how the tissues look when seen in their gross external form; he pushes the microscope deep, follows patterns of cells, threads and fibres, describes and sketches them, with the final aim of showing how they work. Ever since he possessed his own microscope, his French textbook, and his microtome, Santiago had learned the technique. Now, a relatively prosperous professor in Valencia, he purchased an improved microtome, and subscribed to one more scientific periodical the *Journal de l'Anatomie et de la Physiologie*.

The first problem was to bring his subject matter within reach of the microscope. The geologist has a method of boring and blasting in order to find the nature of the earth's crust. The histologist too has to fetch up his materials from out of the depths. Except in rare cases, he can only examine a tissue when it is dead, fixed and stained. Even when this is done, he must magnify his preparation fifty or a hundred times, and it is impossible to see anything at all unless a strong beam of light is thrown through the tissue, so that it looks like a stained glass window illuminated from the further side. How he made these thin cuttings of tissue, their staining, and the careful study of what lies behind what can be seen — this is the story of Cajal's professional work for the next forty years. Merely to prepare materials and describe them — it sounds so easy. Yet the difficulties constantly baffled him, and in the end, many problems remained unsolved. No impression can be faithful unless it conveys a sense of the effort, the bewildering obstacles and the stubborn resistance of those tiny specks of tissue.

His first work in Valencia was concerned with the very simplest of tissues — the skin, muscles, fibrous strands. They can be called simple only when compared with the fantastic complication of the brain tissues that he examined when he had mastered his technique.

Let us imagine ourselves in the home laboratory of the Professor's house in the *Calle de los Avellanos*. Watch him as he sits at a common kitchen table that would today be thought sadly inadequate, with a few homely bottles, the microscope, sketchbook, and a carefully sharpened razor fixed in the microtome. He had the faculty of working patiently for hours and days. The methods of histology were dull and laborious. But its achievements were exciting.

He takes a tiny fragment of an organ or tissue, about the size of a pea. It is soft, pulpy, perhaps semi-liquid, and must first be rendered solid, so that the razor can cut slices of thinness sufficient for light to shine through. The earliest method had been to freeze the whole lump and then to shave off several sections. Later this gave way to paraffin impregnation which produces a more reliable result. The fragment of tissue is placed in a small bowl of warm liquid wax, and this works its way into every nook and cranny of the tissue, a process requiring several days. The wax has now replaced the water in the tissue, and every part of it is firmly supported. When the paraffin enclosing the tissue has cooled and hardened, it has now the consistency of a wax candle. A small block holding the tissue (which is imprisoned inside it like a chicken in jelly) is placed in the microtome. This instrument is a kind of guillotine, having a razor, upon the edge of which the paraffin block is manœuvred up and down, each time fractionally nearer the blade, so that the razor shaves off a series of thin wafers which are then placed one by one flat on glass slides. Cajal had no need to learn the use of a razor as a tool. Señor Acisclo in the barber's shop had taught him that. When the wax has been carefully melted away by warming, nothing remains but the tissue, adhering to the glass slide, and perfectly translucent.

Spread over his working table were numerous sections in different stages of preparation. Next came the staining. Unless the section were coloured, the rays of light shine through each part of it indifferently, and the eye is unable to make out the detail. The section must be chemically treated, with a dye that possesses an affinity for particular elements in the tissue. By staining, the histologist obtains his finest effects. In beautiful contrast, certain fibres might stand out, crimson against a background of blue. He traces them out in contrast to other parts that remain pale or colourless.

Staining is to the microscopist what the palette is to the landscape painter — with this difference, that in histology, the aesthetic effect of colour is subordinate to the convenience of sharp contrasts. Only when the staining is complete does the real work of histology begin. With his eye down the microscope, a finger twisting the screw that changed the focus, and his beard touching the paper, Cajal explored every corner of the slide, and made a careful drawing. That eye and hand whose hunger for visual reality had so angered Don Justo, was now the histologist's finest tool. An art with coloured crayons, combined with a craftsman's skill in making sections, constituted a double asset such as no professor in Spain possessed.

Shaving off slivers no larger or coarser than postage stamps, staining and drawing them, he spent all his days. In his approach to his work, there was something rude and tenacious. For many years, Cajal had just to blunder along, learning from doing, for textbooks left much unexplained. It was a laboursome way of acquiring knowledge, but it favoured originality. Cajal worked all day, being too much of a northerner to require that lengthy siesta to which they are accustomed in the indolent south; and in the evening, he played chess in the café. Valencia was full of intelligent conversationalists. Among them Cajal may have come across a younger man, a law student named Vicente Blasco Ibanez, whose tempestuous career of Radical agitation ended in exile, but who was better known for his novels. There were many such Liberals in talk and action. However outspoken over chess, however original in his theories about art, life and science, Ramon y Cajal was not a revolutionary.

In Valencia, he was happy and popular, and was now ready to make his first bow to the scientific world outside the Iberian peninsula, for he had discovered with some bitterness, that world science did not speak Spanish.

French had taken the place of Latin as the tongue of European culture although it was giving way to German. In French, Cajal composed his first paper addressed to the great world — actually his fifth scientific communication. He sent it to the well-known anatomist Wilhelm Krause of the University of Göttingen who was editor of a German monthly organ, *The Journal of Anatomy and Physiology*, which had also an edition published in London. The paper was accepted in 1885, and Cajal's drawings seemed to Krause of such merit that he agreed to pay for the lithographic reproductions instead of requiring the author to pay.

Today, the volume of that learned journal has the period flavour of a horse carriage, for science grows quickly out of date. Yet Cajal's first paper, though simple compared to what was to come later, will not lose its essential truth. It deals with the type of cells that cover the surface of the body, and describes their outline, shape, and mode of being connected to one another by fibrous links. It was a primary, a fundamental theme. Those monochrome illustrations made from pencil drawings, which so impressed Wilhelm Krause are plain and workmanlike, but have none of the brilliance of Cajal's later work. He grew very slowly to his greatness. He entered the world of histology humbly.

He had opened his mouth in the hearing of every histologist in the world. They were a small group, fifty perhaps, who were capable of appreciating its value. They would meditate upon his description of the cells of the skin, and assign him a status in their narrow and expert circle. By being admitted by the great Wilhelm Krause into his journal, Cajal had earned the right of serious consideration. Like a singer performing before a select audience of the greatest artists, he received a highly critical evaluation.

After a few weeks, that month's issue of the *Journal of Anatomy and Physiology* would be replaced by the next, and find its way on to a shelf. Thereafter, from time to time, it might be consulted by some learned specialist who needed to know what that Spanish fellow — with the unpronounceable name — had reported about the epithelial cells in 1885. Cajal's name grew more frequent in indexes, each year with a longer list of publications attached. Copies of that first article went to Zaragoza, and became favourite reading of the old anatomist Don Justo, proud to realize that his own greatest contribution to science had been his eldest son.

There was other good news for him and Donna

Antonia. The wild Pedro was alive. In years of silence he had lived and fought with the *Indios* in the forests of Paraguay. Every danger of the jungle had become known to him in those incredible adventures. He was wounded, recovered, he wrote dispatches for an Indian chieftain, but for ten years he wrote no letters home. Then as suddenly as he had left, Pedro returned to Spain and took up his career as a medical student.

CHAPTER XXI

THE SILVER STAIN

THOSE credulous dreamers, the alchemists, believed that the influence of a metal could dominate a man's life. In such a pattern of destiny Ramon y Cajal's metal would certainly have been silver: silver as used in photography (which today accounts for one-fifth of the employment of this metal in the world), and also as a stain for the tissues. As a boy in the crypt of St. Teresa's in Huesca, he had been captivated by the magic of the image slowly appearing out of the dark yellow surface. He had become expert in photography, and even in the manufacture of sensitive plates. Now at the end of his career in Valencia, silver turns up once again, and the episode demands to be taken slightly out of chronological order.

A colleague, Dr. Luis Simarro, a psychiatrist, returning from a visit to Paris, brought something to show Cajal. It was a cutting of brain tissue, stained according to the formula of an Italian, Professor Camillo Golgi of the University of Pavia. Cajal stared through the microscope at the arrangement of brain cells. Only in romantic terms can the emotional intensity of Cajal's vision be described. He was never half-hearted when he examined a new preparation. Here was something unique . . . Cells and fibres were clear and sharp, as though drawn in Chinese ink upon transparent Japanese paper, the cells dark brown and the fibres jet black. Next day, he returned to Dr. Simarro's house and asked to examine the slide again. Its beauty, the perfection of

that staining process came as a revelation. The brain
was a tissue which he himself had attempted to stain,
with crude vegetable dyes like *Carmine* and *Haematoxylin*,
but his results, as compared to the brilliance of Golgi's
preparation, had been like a watery twilight. He
borrowed from his friend a copy of a paper in Italian,
and began to try the technique at his own bench. The
tissue had to be treated for several days in a solution of
bichromate, followed by silver nitrate, and in the
marriage between the two, silver bichromate was
produced. Those threads of jetty black against the
fawn-coloured background were really metallic silver
which possesses an affinity for nerve cells and fibres,
and has the power to render them clearly visible, in the
same way as the lines and shadows become visible in a
photographic plate when 'developed'. Golgi's process of
staining was identical with that of photography: the
same use of silver, the same effect through 'developing'.

This Italian professor was a man eleven years older
than himself, who had worked on brain cells long before
Cajal emerged from Zaragoza. Camillo Golgi was
undoubtedly a pioneer, but he lacked Cajal's single-
minded passion for pure histology. He turned aside to
other matters — malaria and national politics. There
was a contributory reason why Cajal should have
overlooked Golgi's method. The Italian language, as a
vehicle of science was discounted as much as Spanish,
and Golgi's early paper had been published in an
obscure Italian journal. Cajal had paid the penalty of
being too inclined to look for novelties only in French
and German. Now, with his usual concentration, that
discipline of over-valuation which had once made him
an athlete, he began to stain everything by the silver

process. The nervous system — brain and spinal cord — was indeed a new realm, opened up to travellers by that pioneering voyage of Camillo Golgi who had lost interest in his new world and hardly bothered to revisit it.

The more he used the silver method, Ramon y Cajal found its limitations. At its best, the process threw up the nerve cells with magnificent clearness; like a drawing of a tree in which each branch, twig and leaf is perfectly delineated. In the next tissue he examined, after identical treatment, the result was a failure. The silver stain had misbehaved. Its results were in fact unpredictable, and it was this, no doubt, which had caused Camillo Golgi to abandon it.

The outside observer might imagine that science in action would always follow scientific rules. Yet every worker in a laboratory soon learns, at bitter cost, that sometimes a devil takes hold of his material. Some perverse contradiction causes his carefully thought out methods to give opposite results. A formula that works well today, will be negative tomorrow. That tantalizing eccentricity of inert matter has caused many a promising idea to fail. When he challenges nature, the research worker has to bear with her resistance and her idiosyncrasy.

This situation was one with which the tenacious spirit of Ramon y Cajal seemed especially made to deal. If you had told him there were a difficulty beyond the reach of will power, a burst of flame would come to his large brown eyes. Like a peasant who has not money enough to buy a spade, he would begin to tear at the earth with his naked hands. In the course of some years, we shall see him convert the method of the dilettante Golgi into a creative instrument that revolutionized knowledge of the brain.

But this is still many years in the future.

Before Golgi's method had captured his whole interest, Ramon y Cajal passed through a crisis that almost led him to abandon histology altogether. Extraneous circumstances connected with that Arabian water supply in the old city of Valencia broke into his peace and compelled him to make a change in the objects on his working table.

The Professor and father of a young family, who was becoming a familiar in the cafés but otherwise a dark horse, was obliged to specialize in a department of knowledge as novel as atomic medicine today. Cholera had burst upon Valencia, with all the horror of a supernatural visitation. It was Asiatic cholera from the East Mediterranean. The phenomena were swift and terrifying; diarrhoea, a fever, and death in a couple of days. It had travelled with the speed of cargo ships from Calcutta, to Bombay; it reached Egypt in 1883, being carried the following year to Europe. It began like an attack of food poisoning. It ended like a shot from a rifle. Family doctors were grave but confused, holy oils were called for, funeral bells tolled frequently. In 1885 medical practice in this sinister *cholera morbus* inspired no comfort; at the start of an outbreak there would be an argument between physicians as to whether a case were really the genuine cholera. As the epidemic made the answer plain, there arose disputes as to whether to give, or withhold opium, a blessed drug which alleviated the horror, but did not cure. That summed up contemporary experience.

Yet, precise knowledge there was, even in 1885, though as yet no more than abstract science that had still to be applied to local conditions. Families had begun to flee to the hills, and the subdued yet unmistakable essence of panic, never to be forgotten by anyone who has ever watched an epidemic, paralysed the wits of those who should lead public opinion. In this penumbra of fear, definite, accurate knowledge is a wonderful reassurance. The histologist in the *Calle de los Avellanos* turned aside from his sections. Ramon y Cajal had read in German medical journals that the great Robert Koch had been summoned by the Khedive of Egypt to investigate an outbreak of *cholera morbus*, on the banks of the Nile. Applying the famous technique which had led him to find the cause of tuberculosis, Koch announced in July 1884 to a conference in Berlin his 'comma' bacillus (so called because of its curved shape), as the true cause of cholera. Now, in his laboratory, Cajal followed Koch's directions for growing the germ on plates of nutrient jelly. His room housed live cultures enough to kill the whole of Valencia. Since this bacillus was conveyed from human carriers to others via that water supply which was still managed in the tradition of Arabian democracy, it was an obvious precaution to boil every drop of water before use. This simple preventive kept his own family safe, despite the presence of live cultures in the house. Ramon y Cajal turned aside from his histology, and wrote two papers upon the 'comma' bacillus, which were published one in Zaragoza, and one in the local medical journal of Valencia. He introduced a rapid culture method which enabled the organism to be recognized early.

Next to the boiling of water, the most important application of Robert Koch's ideas lay in vaccination, that is in protecting the body in advance by injecting a carefully measured number of killed germs. Vaccination in theory had been in vogue for nearly a hundred years

since Edward Jenner used it to prevent smallpox, and
Cajal saw that the same idea could be applied to cholera.
It was new, and perhaps risky, and the older doctors in
Valencia were much opposed. Some younger members
of the profession wished to form a syndicate to manufacture cholera vaccine upon a commercial basis and
they pressed Ramon y Cajal to join them. Though he
believed in cholera vaccination, he hesitated.

He was not really interested in commercial applications.
Though he always claimed to have originated cholera
vaccination, the theory attracted him more than its use.
Besides, there was another, more fundamental point. If
people would only boil their water— the danger of cholera
would virtually disappear. To Ramon y Cajal, the scientific side of the controversy was the most important side—
to study the growth and habits of this 'comma' bacillus,
which, despite its appalling lethal power, is easily killed; to
apply the one elementary preventive measure of destroying it in the water supply— such seemed to him the correct
philosophy to apply to this epidemic.

Such an attitude proclaims the genuine scientist of
medicine, a type not so common in 1885 as today.
Ramon y Cajal's two papers had attracted attention. An
Austrian scientist had stated that the cholera bacillus
produces spores (a particularly resistant phase of growth
found with some germs) but Cajal disproved this theory,
and his view has been upheld. This and his advocacy of
vaccination, had given him an original place in cholera
research.

Even Zaragoza was prepared to acknowledge him as a
favourite son. His friends there asked him to lecture
upon precautions to safeguard the city. He was strongly
tempted to be drawn into bacteriology. His daily

routine would have been much the same. Instead of staining sections, he would spread cultures of germs upon nutrient jelly — that was all the difference, and his expertness with the microscope would be essential still. The irresolute performance of Golgi's silver stain had discouraged him; and this new prestige both in Valencia and Zaragoza, were strong practical arguments in favour of renouncing histology.

The dilemma did not last for long. When the cholera panic died down, Ramon y Cajal returned to his tissues and stains. What seemed to others a dead study had cast over him a living spell. Such dedication is one of the signs of talent. To flit from one subject to another, with the illusion of keeping up to date, is evidence of infirmity of will power. Cajal's powers had been slow in growth, but now they had matured. Besides, there was in histology a motive that he found in no other part of medicine, the aesthetic motive. To watch those tiny sections flowering under his hand as he stained them in brilliant colours, to trace on paper with crayons and reproduce in journals by lithograph the superb complexity of those webs of tissue — that was a profound satisfaction. Bacteriology, which offered fewer pictorial opportunities, never had any permanent hold over his imagination. There was also an economic argument. To study germs required a Noah's Ark of animal victims, and an expensive incubator.

Apart from the two papers, on the cholera bacillus, his only memento of the epidemic of 1885 was the modern Zeiss microscope (greatly superior to the one he was using) which was presented by his friends in Zaragoza, as a tribute to his distinction, and the practical advice he had given to their city.

CHAPTER XXII

QUEEN OF CATALONIA

IN a few short years Ramon y Cajal had greatly improved his professional abilities. He was no longer an unknown from the north, a wandering friar of a despised science. Histology had come into fashion, was being considered essential as part of medical education. The young man in love with a young subject found that it grew up with him. Once more he was a successful candidate in the *oposiciones*, and before him they placed the embarrassing choice between Zaragoza and Barcelona, for in each University there was a vacant chair.

Zaragoza, capital of Aragon, called him with all its old magic. In that ancient city he had dreamed, read, and loved: It was the scene of his foolish pranks and his intellectual awakening, the place where he married his girl with the Marguerite's hair and geranium cheeks. For years he had laboured there, beside his father, and learned to use his first microscope. Family compulsions, arguments from Don Justo, familiarity, and sentiment were pulling him strongly. Yet, as he thought of it, he began to have doubts. Would not Zaragoza, with the proprietary instinct of an ancient relative, set him back to where he had once been, merely a local product and old Don Justo's boy? As a distinguished visitor from Valencia, they had presented him with a Zeiss microscope. Would it be the same if he settled among them? The alternative choice was Barcelona, Queen of Catalonia. There was also a question whether the Catalonians would accept him.

This beautiful city on the sea was loved throughout the north-east of the peninsula with the sort of love a Scotsman feels for Edinburgh. At one glorious moment of history, Barcelona had rivalled Venice and Genoa, her commercial empire extending as far as Greece. Even in 1887, the Catalan city kept a bracing intellectual spirit, and still spoke her ancient language. The Catalans are the Aberdonians of Spain, energetic, thrifty, tenacious; and where two of them meet, they are likely to speak with enthusiasm of fellow Catalans, tracing to their superior merits every good thing done in Iberia, and referring to Madrid as though it might be Buenos Aires. In deciding upon Barcelona, Ramon y Cajal cannot have felt any real hesitation, and no doubt Don Justo was secretly content that the background of his own early poverty should be the scene of his son's triumph. Barcelona remembered the new Professor hailed from Aragon, and accepted him.

Barcelona was the most 'modern' city in Spain, though it had imitated some of the bad features of Victorian England.

The mental climate was more stimulating than Valencia, but opportunities for medical investigation were mediocre. The overcrowded hospital of *La Santa Cruz* was more ancient monument than an efficient centre of healing. Lacking any more convenient situation, Cajal set up his working bench in his own house in the *Calle del Bruch*. Here in a tranquil atmosphere, looking out upon a garden, he surrounded himself with the tools of histology. Fortunately, he has left a charming self-portrait taken by camera. The Professor can be seen as it were on the threshold of his greatest accomplishment. He wears a kind of rustic smock, gathered in folds across his chest at a line below the arms with the sleeves turned up, and on his head sits a round professorial hat, flattened on the top. The oval, still young face had a short pointed beard, and the eyes, cast down, rest upon a drawing which he has just completed. The plain table is covered with a cloth, and we see that single one-tubed microscope which today would be a quaint exhibit in a museum. The scene has an amateur, almost a domestic touch, which gives insight into Ramon y Cajal. He was a lone craftsman, who used homely methods, like those seventeenth-century artists who turned out those incomparable enamelled snuff-boxes from tiny workshops. With such primitive tools, and mental qualities, equally primary, he built up his extraordinary success.

What was its secret? The discipline which proved effective in the muscle-training period of Zaragoza had now flowered into a definite working plan. Cajal's habit was to throw into everything ten times the effort strictly necessary. He was never content to sketch from one slide where ten slides would do. He over-valued, concentrated. Where another histologist would be content to observe one single tissue, he demanded specimens from an enormous range of animal species. No more methodical observer has ever looked down a microscope, yet an impetuous imagination stormed every obstacle in rapid spurts of energy. He was resolved to investigate every variety of living tissue throughout the entire animal kingdom — skin, muscle, internal organs — leaving over till the last, because of its immense complexity, the brain and spinal cord. That was to be his *magnum opus*, to be attained only after much self-education, and approached with an almost feverish reverence.

A lifetime was not too long for such an exploration, a lifetime of solitude such as gives to the passionate worker an illusion of complete freedom.

Laborious solitude in the laboratory allowed the concentration necessary for a scientific man; yet carried to excess, it made professors stupid. Ramon y Cajal was lost in his own perfectionism, yet he had a horror of those who became prisoners in their own expertize. By nature he had strong gregarious feelings, and he loved talking. In Barcelona the men frequented cafés, and after lunch or before dinner satisfied over innumerable cups of coffee the Spanish ardour for brisk and interminable discussion. Among politicians, artists and business men Cajal could relax. In authoritarian Spain, the talk over marble-topped tables is free and uninhibited. In the *Café de Pelayo*, they defended and attacked liberalism — it being the privilege of men in cafés to question ideas that the Church took for granted. Darwinism for instance — it was still a novel and transcendental sort of dogma, but was it in accord with Holy Catechism? Certainly not. They discussed new writers — such as the terrible Schopenhauer — who had as much as said the human will was supreme, and the diabolic Nietzsche whose new superman had many attributes of the animal. Above all, they discussed Iberian politics, using their own Catalan tongue so long suppressed by the centralizing foolishness of those politicians in Madrid. In Barcelona, each man was a private revolutionary, though always convinced that one Catalan was superior to ten Castilians. Ramon y Cajal's voice was fierce and frequent.

When the principal combatants had discharged their arguments, the waiter would bring out the pieces, and with a chosen partner, Cajal opened a game of chess. The match would continue the next day, and the next, and a circle of watchers formed to admire Don Santiago's audacious strategy. Strangers would ask to meet him, and presently, he was able to take on four opponents simultaneously. His reputation grew, he was invited to the Officers' Club, where it pleased him to astonish those open-eyed military men by playing with his eyes shut. Cajal's visual faculty (well developed by histology) could easily retain the tactical position in several games at once.

Spain has always produced great masters of this noble game. The greatest of them, Don Ruy Lopez y Philidor, had also been a bishop. Cajal found in chess a mental stimulation and scope for his native pugnacity. He read books upon the science, then carefully tested each rule in action. When the game was over, he would rise from the chess board in a state of intellectual intoxication, four solutions competing in his mind, over-excited by coffee. Back at his bench in the *Calle del Bruch* the cerebral over-excitement would continue. He would still move his queen, safeguard his knights and work out a lengthy manœuvre to protect a single pawn. As he examined a tissue under the microscope, the black and white squares obtruded, and in place of cells, he saw the complex order of the chessmen. The noble science had ceased to be a game; it had become an obsession. Sometimes a nightmare of rooks and bishops roused him from sleep, and he would shout aloud to his second self, that bungling player of the *Casino Militar*, 'You idiot, why did you not checkmate in the fifth move?'

Instead of being a rest, chess was wearing him out. He foresaw his addiction growing to an uncontrollable mania, turning him into one of those obese habitués who are chained to the chess board until one day, apoplexy removes them, and are promptly replaced, being no more valued than the leg of a table. He decided, very solemnly, to renounce the game altogether, yet he must do this without losing face. He was sensitive over his reputation in the *Café de Pelayo*. To conquer this chess neurosis, it was necessary to retire with honour. Whenever he lost a game, his egotism demanded revenge, and he would go on again playing till he won. In the final flourish to precede his final retirement, one resounding victory was essential. An obstacle to this was his own natural exuberance. Cajal's personal style was full of natural dash which expressed itself in wild gambits that often led to defeat. Now, to make victory inevitable, he cunningly transformed his mode of play. Casting aside all risks, he followed the crafty and deliberate strategy of the old masters. Instead of Ramon y Cajal, he became the reincarnation of Don Ruy Lopez, that cautious traditionalist. The manœuvre had a remarkable effect. For a whole week, he never lost a single game. Honour had been satisfied, and he could now make his final bow.

The Professor rose from the table, saluted the officers, and never handled a chess piece for twenty-five years.

CHAPTER XXIII

PALM SUNDAY

T H E Professor in Barcelona approached the hour
of recognition for the vitality of his subject. His fear
of poverty implanted by Don Justo had faded in
the warmth of worldly acclaim. He had the assurance
that, short of a revolution (a possibility often mentioned
nevertheless in the cafés) he was secure in a material
sense. It was, at the age of thirty-six, a satisfaction for a
country boy who began with nothing. Yet, in such
triumph there was a risk — that of diminishing future
activity. Those who have begun life hard often grow
fatigued early, and sometimes take revenge for previous
hardships by embracing too closely the first enjoyment of
success. In Cajal the danger was not idleness in its crude
form. He was too intense and methodical. Games of
chess in the *Café de Pelayo* had been sternly renounced,
but there were other forms that mental lassitude might
assume. A man of science could be as lazy with the
microscope as any *boulevardier* over the chess board.
The delights of the intellectual life, the temptation to
repeat what is already complete, constitutes a subtle
risk for the professor who has 'arrived'.

In one sense, his increasing technical excellence was
itself a pitfall. It is tempting to repeat what one does
well. He was a master with the razor, the stain and the
pencil. He was entitled to feel pleasure in the cunning
of hand and eye that had been awakened in such strange
circumstances. To create an enduring work, a man
needs more than a clever technique. He needs a mighty

theme, greater than his technique, greater than himself.

The year 1888 was to be what Cajal called his Palm Sunday. It was indeed a triumphal entry into a new field of brain histology, though it was no more than the entry. The first hosannas which greeted his papers on the nervous system, were only a prelude. More was to follow, years of work, theories, disappointments, attacks — before he was recognized as the foremost scholar in the world, in the structure of the brain.

To consider his achievement in its proper relation, it is necessary to realize that until the end of the nineteenth century there existed virtually no knowledge either of brain function, or of how brain was related to mind. It never occurred to the ancient philosophers that the physical brain might be studied like a machine. In all the generations during which man had observed himself, the brain remained a closed book. Aristotle made the beginnings of psychology, and Plato the foundation of ethics; Descartes and Emanuel Kant had evolved magnificent theories of mind, coherent explanations of such philosophical entities as thought, purpose, will and emotion. Hardly any further generalization seemed possible that had not been anticipated. Yet through centuries, the physical organ of the brain remained virgin territory, apart from some descriptive attention which the old anatomists had given its crude structures, and of which Don Justo had taught elegant names, such as *hippocampus*, *pons*, or *thalamus*.

The early histologists had begun to examine brain sections, in England, France and Germany, especially the last, and the Universities were already centres of research that slowly trickled into medical journals. The brain tissue it was found, consisted of an infinite number of special nerve cells, and an infinite number of nerve fibres, and arranged in bunches like the wires of a telephone exchange. Patience, and discrimination was needed to study this complex machine, part by part. At first, increasing knowledge produced increasing confusion. Each nerve cell and fibre is of course microscopic, and the preparation and staining of paraffin sections means that only an infinitesimal fraction of the brain can be examined at one time. The tracing of millions of fibres which sometimes extend several inches in length, was a task of unbelievable difficulty. This new world awaited a conqueror and an interpreter. Ramon y Cajal pinned his faith to Camillo Golgi's silver stain. It was often a will-o'-the-wisp. Could it be made to function as a searchlight?

In that year he called his Palm Sunday — 1888 — Ramon y Cajal published in all, nine papers, of which six were upon the brain and other parts of the nervous system.

CHAPTER XXIV

THE BRAIN CELLS

BRAIN is the organ of destiny. Those fifty ounces of soft brain matter inside our skulls, which represent man's sole claim to uniqueness in the animal kingdom and his only means of further superiority, consist of at least ten thousand millions of separate cells, of a highly specialized character. Between these cells, day and night, from before birth, until death ends their activity, surge restless tides and currents of electricity, which when measured amount to less than one-hundredth of one volt. Through them we speak a definite cerebral pattern or brain language, unknown in the 1880s, although the electrical mechanism of the brain was beginning to be suspected. Cajal's work lay in isolating and drawing those brain cells and fibres, describing their pattern and adumbrating their function. To get an idea of his originality, we must picture what the histologist before Cajal saw when he looked at a cutting of brain tissue. A convenient analogy is that of a tropical forest. We abandon, therefore, for the present, those previous analogies of electric wires, and substituting a green solid wall of trees, the mind will grasp the formidable problem of brain histology, namely the complexity of the brain cells and connections.

Let us suppose a botanist facing a wall of green forest, say in Cuba, or in the *Matto Grosso*, were to attempt to work out the distribution of the different species of trees. Not merely to count them, for that would be impossible, but to discover the prevailing plan of the vegetation, and how the trees are formed, what pattern their roots make, and how their leaves are arranged. From the outside, the botanist sees nothing but a dense mass of vegetation. At closer examination, he finds the forest is composed of innumerable trees of different kinds, seemingly intertwined with one another, and connected by trailing twisting creepers. Below the soil, their roots compete for moisture. Anyone not a botanist might be forgiven for thinking that the forest was indeed one continuous and consistent mass of growing vegetation.

Let us, now, transfer the comparison to an actual brain section, taking it say from the cortex (or outer layer only a few millimetres thick), where lie, closely packed, the centres of human thought, feeling, and motion. Like the trees in a forest, each cell is quite independent from the rest, yet it appears to be connected with others by masses of fibres, in the same way as the lianas of the *Matto Grosso* connect between trees.

When we think, we use not one cell, but millions. The simplest memory, the most insignificant jerk of a finger, or the recognition of day passing into night — causes electrical flashes to pass between whole groups of cells, at a speed that seems instantaneous. Only in this way can the mind produce a synthesis of recognition, act, and memory, or countless other functions. As for a mathematical calculation, writing a music symphony — they involve cerebral processes almost beyond analysis. Lightning associations, are formed into memories, feelings, judgments, while the mind plays upon this enormous material and effects a synthesis. Everything is achieved through the rapidity of communication. Later, it will be obvious that these highly specialized functions are possible only through a highly complex pattern.

Cajal's work was to organize chaos, and patiently describe and elucidate the cells themselves.

At first sight, the brain structure appeared to be, as with other organs of the body, a network of fibres criss-crossing like the threads in cloth. Junctions were everywhere, between cells and fibres, and between fibres and cells. Such was the prevailing conception among the earlier histologists — the 'network' theory. It was based upon inaccurate observation, and the truth was very different, as will appear.

Secure in his technique, Cajal examined hundreds of sections, in man and animals. He was fascinated, yet appalled at their infinite variety. There was for instance — one particular group in which each cell sent down its thread-like projection that hung in the manner of a chandelier. Similar fibre threads came upward from further cells, and while they spread themselves around the body of the first cell, they never actually touched. He made sections of the electric organ of the torpedo fish, that dynamo of the rivers which, when alarmed can send out 600 volts. There inside that electric lobe which generates the currents, there were the specialized cells, each really a tiny battery having thousands of branching terminals. Each of the separate electric cells generates a minute charge of electricity. Together they make up to 600 volts. Yet each cell battery and its thread-like wire remains a separate unit. None of them when individually examined, was seen to join up with the network. Such a paradox was found everywhere in the nervous system.

It was an extraordinary contradiction to the first impression. Seen in the mass, the nervous tissues appeared to prove the 'network' theory beyond all doubt. Yet whenever a single fibre could be isolated, it was never seen to join the others, but only to continue its own course, discrete and independent. To unify these opposites, reconciling them into a single doctrine of nerve structure, it was necessary to use staining methods that would pick out a single nerve pathway, isolate it from the next, so that the observer's eye could follow the pathway through the mass. Good staining was essential, and using Camillo Golgi's silver, Cajal was able to throw a searchlight on each separate cell unit, leaving the rest in obscurity.

We can return now to the analogy of the tropical forest, and see how this bridges the gap between the 'network' theory, and the isolated individualism of single fibres which Cajal observed. The botanist who wished to analyse the pattern of the trees might begin by selecting a single species of tree — say an evergreen oak — out of the mass of arboreal vegetation, and follow out its distribution, pursuing each example from its terminal branches and the extremity of its roots. He would certainly conclude that each tree is a separate unit of life. Leaves and roots may touch by accident, but they remain independent in structure.

In principle, Ramon y Cajal's technique was exactly the same: to isolate the evergreen oaks from the others, examining one tree at a time. It was a simple scheme — when properly understood — and like Columbus's way of making an egg stand on its end, it appeared the easiest thing in the world, once it had been achieved. His method was applied in two stages; the first to use different animal tissues, following in each the particular cell (the oak tree) and searching for analogies between them, as it were in many actual forests. By comparing like with like, and like with unlike, from birds, fishes, worms and insects, he assembled from a prodigious body of facts a doctrine which covered the whole of animal nature. One bit of information would come from the retina of a bird's eye, another from the frog. Muscles of a worm might have nerve connections that were easy to observe. Mammals of different species gave confirmation of particular points. He was delighted to find that the nerve unit was common to the whole animal kingdom, although with nature's usual prodigality of resource and her utter indifference to wasteful experiment, they differed enormously in their form. Still, nature's master plan was recognizable in all the animal tissues. So much for the first stage in Cajal's research.

The second original stage was his use of tissues from the embryo. It was as though our botanist, in order to simplify his task, and despairing of ever being able to accomplish anything in the full-grown forest, had found a 'virgin nursery' of trees in which the different species could be examined at an early and simpler stage of growth, when they were merely shoots and slips. Imagine a part of the Amazon basin while as yet the trees were only saplings, before they had become matted and joined together. There would be none of the hopeless tangle of the mature forest, and he would be able to pick out the oaks — keeping them quite apart from cedars, mangoes and mahogany trees. Such a simplification Cajal achieved by using embryonic tissues.

He discovered the cardinal law of nervous structure.

The fact is, nerve fibres arise from a parent cell, and never join other cells. They do not even come into organic contact. They meet, and the tiny interval between one and another is bridged only by an electrical discharge which jumps from one to another in the manner of a current leaping across a 'spark-gap'. Over this fundamental fact, was to rage one of the fiercest battles in biology, during which Cajal found himself in an embarrassing position with Golgi, to whose silver bichromate he owed those brown-black preparations that were so revealing.

The fact that nerve fibres do not join makes possible the most delicate operations of the brain. It is not too much to say that this is what gives man his miraculous potentiality in the development of his mind.

Camillo Golgi was to be hoist with his own petard. The silver stain works even better in the embryo than in the adult, though its inventor had not known this. This perfect instrument for investigation was to be the means of disproving Golgi's favourite 'network' theory. This fundamental error was not overthrown at once, but in the year which Ramon called his Palm Sunday, when he was still a new professor at Barcelona, there dawned a fame that was to spread over Europe, like some pervasive song of his troubadour ancestors in the days of Languedocian culture.

CHAPTER XXV

RECOGNITION IN GERMANY

THAT Lilliputian universe which forms the subject matter of histology is immense, yet in the great world of science, its study was comparatively insignificant, and its professors are rare. A few hundred specialists in Europe and in North America — these were all that were capable of evaluating those articles that came forth from the laboratory in the *Calle del Bruch*. The country where he could count least upon experienced criticism and appreciation was Spain. Copies of papers sent to Spanish colleagues, were received in silence, though later on, Cajal would have the mortification of reading in their subsequent writings statements entirely contrary to facts which he had demonstrated. It was something more than the historic non-acceptance of a prophet in his own home: it was a profound resistance in the Spanish mind to the experimental science, a mistrust amounting to a self-paralysis, of Spanish ability to make discoveries. But other countries were learning the name Ramon y Cajal. He sent reprints to Berlin, Frankfurt, Vienna. In the 1880s German was the language of science, and German-speaking countries its home. To the world where histologists were honoured he had decided to show himself. He set off to attend a conference in Berlin, calling on the way at Frankfurt and Geneva.

His own paper was well received by the meeting; and while the discussion was still going on, he slipped out of the conference hall, set up his microscope to demonstrate some slides he had brought from Barcelona. The other delegates looked upon this slight bearded Spaniard as an oddity. They stared at his preparations, listened to his explanations in French, spoken with the twanging accent of Iberia. They had a certain mistrust of this man with such an unusual name, who was native of a country not strong in science. Cynical Frenchmen, wily Italians were ready to remain quite unimpressed. As for the Germans, they found it almost unthinkable that a non-German could have anything good to show. They gave impatient glances at his sections, as though fearing to be hoaxed. 'Do you do all this with Golgi's stain?' they asked, moving slides to and fro, and noting those dark fibres of each nerve cell as they branched around the cell body of the next. Was all this achieved really by Golgi's method? Such clarity in itself was open to suspicion. They themselves had found the silver stain very capricious. Cajal gave further explanations, while the Frenchmen and Germans searched the slides once more. Then like an eagle among the sparrows appeared among those puzzled histologists the great Professor Albert Kölliker of Wurzburg, the pontiff of microscopic biology. He was by birth a Swiss, but had graduated in Heidelberg, become a German professor, and radiated enormous influence. It was said that Kölliker knew more about the microscopic structure of animal tissues than anyone who ever lived. He was not merely a good observer, but also a theorist, and he wrote textbooks, edited journals and presided over international conferences, with the added prestige of one privileged to use *von* before his name, and to wear the Prussian Order of Merit. The great Kölliker looked at Cajal's preparations, and the overawed bystanders awaited his opinion. It was terse, it was final, it was favourable. He put his arm around Cajal's shoulder. 'I have discovered — you, and I wish to make my discovery known throughout Germany.'

Two worlds had become cross-fertilized. The great Teuton had bestowed upon the Iberian the accolade of acceptance. Ramon y Cajal never forgot that moment, and his reverence for German thought endured throughout his life. Von Kölliker did not confine himself to words. He became a pupil of the Spaniard. He initiated in his own laboratory a series of studies that in time amply confirmed Cajal's work, to which he gave full credit.

Previously, Kölliker had been an adherent of the 'network' theory, but now he was won over by these convincing preparations, and by Cajal's personal charm, and he even talked of learning Spanish. Once the great man had given judgment, everyone else at the conference hastened to follow. They looked again at the slides, found their inhibitions removed and congratulated themselves that first impressions had been correct. Here was a new and great histologist. Everything done with Golgi's stain? *Wunderbar, Herr Kollege. Phénoménal, Monsieur.*

After this triumph, in Berlin Cajal made visits to other German cities and called upon his early patron, Wilhelm Krause of Göttingen, where he was delighted with everything in that famous University — with the exception of a painting supposedly by Velazquez, which he would on no account accept as genuine. German Universities greatly pleased Cajal, by their organization, their academic freedom, their facilities for science. At Göttingen and elsewhere, the professor had his Institute which was his fortress where he ruled as the supreme

commander over a corps of assistants. It was almost
unbelievable to one reared in the individualistic tradition
of Spain where the Universities copied the worst features
of the French system. German professors he found, were
chosen for merit and scientific standing, and they were
officially remunerated according to the importance of
their subject, with fees from students in addition. To one
who had faced *oposiciones*, it was like a dream, and for
many years to come German culture and German
Universities seemed to Ramon y Cajal the highest expression of the European spirit. Even Italy, which he
also visited on the way home, possessed regular endow-
ments for medical research. It was unfortunate that on
passing through Pavia, he should have missed seeing
Camillo Golgi who happened to be absent in Rome,
attending to his duties as *Senatore* of the Kingdom of
Italy. If they had met one another, there would have
been a chance to discuss those elegant preparations made
with the silver stain, and Cajal, whose personality was
like a force of nature, would have had no difficulty in
convincing Golgi of the value of his own method. The
Senatore would have admitted that his stain was the
greatest thing in histology. Alas, that encounter never
took place. It is to be regretted. A mutual understanding on this occasion would have prevented a disastrous
international episode, when years later, the two wor-
shippers of Golgi's stain met face to face.

Throughout this pilgrimage to scientific shrines outside Spain, Cajal's impression was that everywhere, the
Universities were richly endowed as compared with his
own country. There was a further difference to Spain's
disfavour and even less to his taste, yet which was not so
easy to explain. This was psychological, more than

financial. It lay somewhere in the character of the professors themselves. Material advantages were not everything not even in research. There was a feature of even greater import, the character, of the men who filled University chairs. The joy he felt on being home again was tempered by that disturbing thought. Spain needed an academic revival, in ethics as well as organization.

CHAPTER XXVI

THE NEURONE IDEA

HOME in his own garden, the cultivator of histology resumed his work and with furious concentration returned to the quest of its buried riches. The hand of the great Kölliker was still on his shoulder. He felt encouraged. Envy of others, a defect (he felt it to be) of the Spanish character, and the impatience inherited from Don Justo was assuaged by the accolade from the Berlin conference.

The actual labour had become to Cajal a rapture, an enchantment. Those who teach young scientists that the aesthetic emotions have no place in laboratories, are pointing the way to sterility. For Ramon y Cajal, the artistic impulse was a reservoir of power, and a major source of achievement. Those brain cells, with their branching fibres and complex arrangement, were to him real and living as soon as he could draw them. And because he could draw them so well, he understood them clearly. There was no distinction between aesthetic satisfaction and scientific truth. He wrote in his memoirs that cells were as beautiful as flowers; certain of them were like butterflies. The study of the *hippocampus* (a section of the brain) first attracted him by its elegant cell arrangement — like a border of hyacinths in a garden. Some biologists might find such language exalted and unscientific, but to Cajal, the planning of the nervous system exhibited both style and harmony, and his artistic comprehension opened to him many truths that a colder observer would have missed. Reduced to its essentials, this exacting study of the brain cells was a matter of architecture. Later ages would investigate the chemistry, physics, economy of the cell. Ramon y Cajal had first to clear up its form. It was also a problem of aesthetics.

He was now confident of being on the right track, and by the time he came to the age of forty, he had reached his characteristic conception of nerve structure — the 'neurone'. The idea does not belong exclusively to Cajal. It had indeed been developing throughout Europe; and even the term 'neurone' was not his own invention. None the less, Cajal invested in this 'neurone' doctrine his whole life. He threw into it his prestige, his endurance. Cajal became the champion of the 'neurone'. The idea has lasted, and become one of the facts of biology. It belongs to him as securely as radio belongs to Marconi, or the thermionic valve to Ambrose Fleming. We must define clearly what the neurone is.

The 'neurone' is the primary unit of brain structure, and the fundamental of all nervous and mental function. A 'neurone' is a nerve cell plus a nerve fibre which issues from it and is called the *axon*. Out of the cell stick several processes, like spikes or horns. These represent its means of receiving messages from other cells. At the opposite end of its body there grows the *axon* or nerve fibre which may be prolonged, sometimes fifty or a hundred times the diameter of the cell. Nerve cells have an endless diversity of different forms. They can be round, triangular, oblong, and may be large or small. Each part of the brain and spinal cord is composed of different types of cells, and each of them has a different type of *axon*, which with the cell itself makes up a neurone, the fundamental unit of nerve tissue.

At the risk of seeming repetitious it must be said that cell plus *axon* is always independent, separate. However complicated the *axon* fibres may become, they never join a network, never touch other *axons*, however intimate their contact may seem to be. The 'neurone' is thus a nerve unit, which earlier we have compared to an electric battery. The cell itself manufactures a charge of energy; the *axon* discharges it. Later will be seen how Cajal reached this theory of the electrical properties of the cell.

The *axon* extends inches, or even feet until it reaches its intended destination where it communicates with another nerve cell. The terminal of the *axon* frays out into a bunch of hair-like endings. These manage to insinuate their way around the body of another cell, but they never touch. Over the infinitesimal gap between them, the electric current jumps easily, not by contact, but across the free space.

It was years before this unexpected fact of neurone independence could be accepted — even by Ramon y Cajal. Some, like Camillo Golgi, never accepted it at all, but continued to believe that cells and *axons* were all woven into a generalized 'network' throughout the nervous system.

Among the many famous workers who helped to build up the neurone idea, it is surprising to find the name of Sigmund Freud, whose most celebrated discoveries were to be in the more abstract field of instinct and emotion, rather than in the physical structure of the brain. In 1882 Freud, only an impoverished medical student, published a paper, written after experimental work upon the crayfish, which showed that nerve cell and nerve fibre form a single unit. Though he never knew the term 'neurone', he anticipated the idea behind it. Presently, Freud was drawn away into his own characteristic and more metaphysical researches and his paper was forgotten. He was, if not a pioneer of the neurone, at least its prophet.

Although the neurone theory was brought to perfection by Cajal, the word itself was invented, through a stray spark of inspiration, by a different man altogether, one of the great pedagogues of the nineteenth century, Wilhelm Waldeyer of Berlin. He was a Westphalian, Catholic and a master of exposition. Like Cajal, he could cover the blackboard with accurate drawings. Waldeyer's subject was the anatomy of the organs, and not the histology of the tissues, but he had accepted Cajal's doctrine that nerve cells are separate units. In a semi-popular article, he named these units 'neurones'. Since he who gives a thing its name is often considered the real inventor, this happy flash caused Waldeyer to receive the honour of paternity of the neurone, whereas he was only its baptizer. It was a wrong attribution which always irritated Ramon y Cajal.

The full ingenuity, the full beauty of neurone independence becomes clear when we realize that owing to it, each of the ten thousand million cells of the human brain, is potentially in instantaneous communication with each of the others. Though they act in groups, each one really follows its own impulse, and is capable of flashing its message to a far distant group of cells, via the currents passed along those *axons*. If the contrary theory were true and they were all woven into one network, all the cells would be inhibited by other cells. Thanks to their individual isolation (through the existence of a gap between one neurone and the next), there are periods when each may remain passive, completely withdrawn from activity, but ready to resume with full vigour whenever it is to its interest to do so. Neurone independence combines two opposite advantages; instantaneous participation, and complete isolation — which alternate with an ease and flexibility almost beyond our power to conceive. Only because each neurone is independent can the brain act as a whole.

How then does the *axon* from one cell communicate with the cell of the next? We can say it is through an electrical current. Cajal's phrase for it is more expressive. He called it a 'protoplasmic kiss'. Such romantic language seemed to him the only possible way to describe the delicacy of that intimate, yet intermittent, means of communication.

Intense excitement at the discovery of each fresh type of neurone possessed Ramon y Cajal. He was kept awake at night thinking of those cells, shaped like the pyramids of Egypt, that lie on the surface of the brain, the *cortex*. How did it all come to be? At some early point in the aeonal history of evolution, insects, reptiles, birds had developed those humbler mechanisms which foreshadowed the human brain. Seen as a whole, that immense evolution from the lower creature up to the human being was easy to comprehend. When examined in detail, it showed nothing but confusion. As he worked out neurone architecture, the permutations seemed endless.

The neurone, its integrity and its ramifications obsessed him. He narrowed his gaze and concentrated upon the principal part of the neurone, the nerve cell itself.

Some observers maintained that the nerve cell and *axon* were merely like opposite ends of a rope stretched between two hooks, and that the fibre grew merely by lengthening the rope. This seemed to Cajal too mechanical a conception. To him, it was clear that the cell dominated the whole process. The nerve cell in fact was the dynamic centre, which pushed out the fibre with the intention of seeking a destination, which it found at last only when those hair-like fibrils had entwined themselves around the next cell body in a delicate basket work. The neurone possesses extraordinary individual force. It is both dynamic and plastic. The *axon* pushes its way along (during the period of growth) by soft and flexible movements that nevertheless have the force of a battering ram, until it reaches the objective. At this point, the growing terminal, hitherto endowed only with a restless faculty of searching, reveals a new talent — that of a permanent embrace. The *axon* possesses the adaptability of the soft shoot of a sycamore tree, which can force its path through concrete when it wishes to follow a particular direction, yet later acquires the power to throw out leaves.

The primitive nerve cell would throw out experimental shoots, and only after several attempts would it reach its particular quarry, and develop its hedge of terminal fibres. Once that was complete, the first hesitating shoots would disappear, as though some supervising gardener had pruned them away. What has been described is of course the growth of the neurones, as he traced them through countless slides. When the body is mature, that growth ceases, and the neurones are permanently fixed.

Ramon y Cajal discovered all this through his technique of examining both animal tissues and those of the human embryo. The novelty of the neurone conception was that the individuality of man goes back to the fundamental independence of each of his nerve units which are endowed with the ability to fight for themselves, and once they are fixed, have the power both of giving and withholding communication with all other neurones. We might say that the neurone is the microcosm of man himself.

There is one final question. What are the habits of the neurone, electrically speaking? Does the current flow out from the cell in all directions? or is it collected by the *axons* and conveyed back to the cell? An answer on this point would complete the doctrine of the neurone.

The more he considered the electrical abilities of the neurone, the greater became the difficulties. No such thing as a 'typical neurone' seemed to exist. These individualistic creatures were seen in such bewildering diversity. It was as though one attempted to generalize between an oak tree and a climbing honeysuckle. The one grew erect and sturdy, the other was insinuating and adaptive. Yet generalization there must be. In the brain, it was common to find, side by side, such totally opposite types of neurone, each intensely specialized for its particular function. How was any general law of electrical function to be discovered between such diverse elements?

Ramon y Cajal decided to summarize it in this way: the nerve cell gathers, by means of its horns and processes, enough energy to originate a great intensification or boosting inside the cell. A charge thus generated then flashes down the *axon* to its furthest end. This is repeated whenever the cell is active. But the direction of the current is always from cell to *axon*, never in the reverse direction. The cell is the battery which makes the charge. The *axon* is the wire which carries the discharge. Cajal called this the law of 'dynamic polarization'.

Can we now gain a general idea of how this complex forest of neurones might appear in action? Each tree, each bush, each trailing creeper, has a unique and separate existence, and maintains that individuality in fierce competition with others. Each possesses roots, branches, and leaves, in the closely packed density of the forest. Though a naive observer might think of it as a continuous mass of vegetation, the botanist knows that each tree is a separate unit of creation. Now, let us imagine a storm passing through that forest. Branches sway in unison, leaves tremble against other leaves, and the huge mass behaves as one organism. A shower of rain occurs; each droplet passing easily from tree to tree. Flashes of lightning sweep over the trees, leaping between wet branches. The whole forest is alive, it writhes and sways, in an epic of unified action. Our naive observer might indeed suppose that the forest were a single mass. The botanist, even with his knowledge of how each tree grows in response to environment, might agree that in certain conditions, such as a storm of rain and lightning, the forest does behave as an organic unity, though this is possible only because each tree had contributed its own individuality.

Such would be the general notion of the way in which the thousand million cells of the human brain work in a perpetual storm of circulating electricity, from before birth until death brings the annihilation of the tissues. Ramon y Cajal had built the foundation upon which all modern research into brain function has become possible.

His Palm Sunday was to lead to an even more jubilant Easter.

CHAPTER XXVII

THE CAFÉS OF MADRID

THE extent of the nervous system is enormous, and Cajal had temporarily moved away from the brain itself to study one of the important nerve tracts called the Sympathetic trunk, which is really a 'main line' conveying nerve impulses to the internal organs. The Sympathetic presented formidable problems. It appeared to be a law unto itself. He was doubtful whether it really possessed proper neurones, and was not merely a bundle of *axon* fibres running down the centre of the body. Cajal was working upon pigeons and doves — and in one instance, he discovered that some cells of the Sympathetic possessed two *axon* fibres in place of the usual one. It was decidedly contrary to what he had believed, and he felt the neurone theory was in jeopardy. With redoubled efforts he prepared more and more slides, and was in fact deeply immersed in the Sympathetic, when distraction came from a different quarter.

A vacancy had occurred in the Chair of Histology and Pathological Anatomy in the University of Madrid. No professor of that science could pretend to be disinterested. Among his many Spanish qualities, the unworldly detachment of the Spanish saints had never been noticeable in Cajal. Once more the tribunal of the *oposiciones* faced him. He might have preferred to stay on in Barcelona, and renounce any desire to be at the heart of affairs. Madrid was certainly the less attractive city, yet its central University had a certain prestige, and

Ramon y Cajal had a driving ambition. Now again, like a junior student, he had to submit himself to a board of professors, answer undiscerning questions, being sure that few of them had read his thirty papers which were accepted in Göttingen and Berlin. He made several appearances before the Tribunal, and he was obliged to withdraw his mind from the Sympathetic, in order to think out his arguments.

His competitors for the Chair were men of ability. To be professor in Madrid was the climax of a teacher's career. A whole-time devotion to the duties was not yet customary in the Medical Faculty, and some of the candidates were wealthy physicians who coveted this academic distinction for the lustre it would shed upon their medical connections. In such professorial elections, there are sometimes good reasons why mediocrity should be preferable to genius. The doubts of the Madrid authorities can be imagined. Cajal is a clever histologist — we admit his brilliance — but is he the true University type, a man who will get on well with other professors? In Madrid, there was a certain prejudice against a man out of Catalonia, who had the reputation for closeting himself closely in his laboratory all day. Ramon y Cajal, never a moderate in his emotions, felt the anxiety of the exceptional man who is obliged to fit into a system made for the average. For this opportunity he had been preparing all his life. He had devoted himself to histology like a Carmelite. He had sketched unweariedly, stained his fingers, strained his eyes, and gone through all the despairs of those who turn their backs upon comforting routine, that solace of many a professor. His beard was beginning to turn white. He had lost all his clinical skill. His professional situation was like that of his mountain birthplace of Petilla de Aragon, cut off from the world except by one narrow bridle path. His one path was the microscope.

The authorities of Madrid University honoured themselves by making a wise choice. They chose Cajal, and secured for their professoriate this man of European fame. Satisfaction in Madrid was balanced by gnashing of teeth in Barcelona where the Faculty realized too late that it was losing a great man. The sweetest triumph was that of the old anatomist, Don Justo Ramon.

What most impressed the new professor on a brief visit to Zaragoza was the surprise on the faces of his old friends as they offered congratulations. Like true provincials, they did not hide their astonishment that the work of a fellow townsman should be accepted in foreign countries.

Every triumph has to be paid for, and on this occasion the forfeit was exacted in a sphere that most deeply offended Cajal's pride. Those cells with double *axons* which he had described in the Sympathetic trunk of mammals — they had been a mistake. No such cells existed. He bitterly regretted the distraction which caused him to publish his paper on the subject without a longer period of study. Upon the Sympathetic, credit went to another histologist.

In Madrid, the saying was, the professors lived without acquaintance and died without mourning. Everyone had innumerable social engagements. The academic circle was hardly circular, and the Medical Faculty lacked cohesion. He missed his friends and acquaintances. When walking along the *Ramblas* of Barcelona, Cajal would be saluted frequently. In Madrid, he was unknown. At first, he could not help feeling the loneliness of a countryman who arrives in the capital city. In Madrid, he missed the sea breezes of the Mediterranean, and it was some time before he became used to the exhilaration of the thin air at two thousand feet, with that wide skyline, glaring sunshine, paralysing winds, and a certain mountain isolation, as though it were some New World capital high up on a plateau of the Andes.

The new professor was obliged to live modestly, because he had now a family of six — but this was no real hardship for a peasant from Aragon. One of Cajal's sayings was — 'Blessed are they who can say No, for they shall live in peace'. This tenacious mountaineer, had never any difficulty in using the negative. Believing that scientific ideas grow best like the water lily — in quiet surroundings — he shut himself up in his new laboratory, and was never seen entering a professional equipage at a patient's front door. Academic colleagues heartily approved of this withdrawal from competition. The Professor of Obstetrics, who happened to be Marquis de Busto and a wealthy man, was so much impressed that he paid over to Cajal his own salary as an endowment for histology.

Aloofness brought mental freedom, and Cajal laboured to efface his mistake over the Sympathetic. The climax of his research was at hand. The cerebellum, the nerves of smell, spinal nerves, the innervation of the heart, the optic nerve in birds — these were his themes. The work of the Palm Sunday period gathered momentum.

Yet Cajal was not by temperament a hermit. His devotion to the microscope had to be balanced by social interchange. He believed that 'the joviality of friends is the best antidote for the venom of the world and the fatigues of life'. Like an *axon* searching for its proper

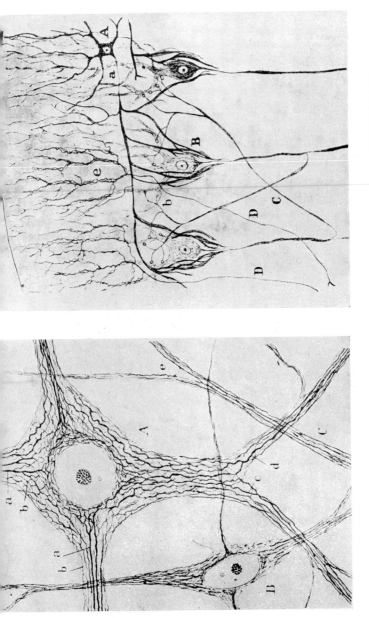

SPINAL CORD CELLS OF RABBIT   CELLS OF CEREBELLUM

Histological drawings of Nerve Cells by Ramon y Cajal

termination, his mind moved towards other minds. The professors in Madrid did not often meet their colleagues upon academic ground, but there were numerous cafés, like clubs in England, where academic men could polish their wits with men of the world. Cajal looked around to find the most congenial centre for his social life.

He tried the *Café de Levante*: it was full of Army doctors obsessed with their professional affairs. These were the men he had known in Cuba, but now twenty years older; they had risen in the Service, but had the same old grievances. The *Café de Levante* was abandoned. He tried other establishments, and finally settled upon the *Café Suizo*. It was a famous resort of intelligence and rhetoric.

Those cafés with their long rooms lined with high mirrors, their crimson plush seats, and chandeliers have disappeared as a force in the intellectual life of Europe. Those marble-topped tables with newspapers and glasses of cognac, the cigar smoke and the waltzes of Johann Strauss, belong to another age. In Spain it was the custom for particular groups of men (in a rigorously masculine society) to hold what were called *tertulias* — sessions of conversational intercourse. For two or three hours a day (before the *siesta*, or after the late dinner) sipping sweet coffee as the Arabs had taught their ancestors, they would talk of politics, women, or business. Other *tertulias* would prefer literature and art, would discuss the satanic operas of Richard Wagner, or the teachings of Henrik Ibsen. At its best, this exchange rose above mere gossip. At its worst, it was not less elevated than the mixed conversation of modern days. The *Café Suizo* had a highly intellectual reputation and to join one of those *tertulias* one needed a formal

K   145

introduction. The members knew of only a few rules, never written, but always respected. A man should discourse solely about what he understood, loquacious pretenders being sternly discouraged. And when he left the table, everything was to be erased from the mind. No consistency, no recriminations, every man being as indiscreet as he liked. Certain groups would centre around some prominent personality, those at neighbouring tables would listen and even the waiters would laugh. Such a man's table was called his *peña*, or rock.

In the *Café Suizo*, the members would watch Don Santiago as he gathered up his arguments, building up a pile of breadcrumbs which presently he discharged with a flip of the forefinger, accompanied by a barrage of justification. Like every Latin, he was a natural orator, and he loved phrases. In later years, he collected in a most successful book, those sayings which had been tried out from his *peña* and afterwards polished in privacy. There was in Cajal a quality not common in clever conversationalists — an ironic awareness of the limitations of human expression. 'Reality', the epigram formed in his mind, 'overflows every concise phrase as liquid poured into a tiny cup.' Nevertheless Don Santiago felt at home and when the *tertulia* finally dissolved in laughter, he felt both relaxed and stimulated.

As we see it now, the 'nineties of last century represent a period of intellectual liberty, of which the café might be taken as a symbol. New theories of art, fresh movements in politics were hatched in places like the *Café Suizo*. Over coffee it was permissible to criticize the King and condemn the Church, since after the *tertulia* all words would have vanished into cigar smoke. There was no need to fear a compulsory sojourn in the Canary Isles.

At the *Café Suizo*, Ramon y Cajal could reveal his mistrust of the Church and need not hide his preference for liberal thought; and he suffered no disadvantage either as a professor or a Spaniard. Would a scientific freethinker have such liberty today?

We may throw backward there a nostalgic glance, and like those interlopers from other tables who leaned over to hear Don Santiago's verbal fencing with the Minister of Education, we marvel at the ease, the wit, the careless authority.

Then the *tertulia* breaks up, the great men separate and the waiters clear away the cups. Those brilliant formulations have evaporated, and because no record was kept, we cannot tell how much, or how little, they would be to the taste of our age.

Yet of one conclusion we can be certain. It was out of the theories of men like Ramon y Cajal over the café tables that our modern scientific and materialistic world has been created.

CHAPTER XXVIII

ENGLAND

THOUGH the members of those *tertulias* argued about the future, they had pride in the past. Their deepest emotions belonged to that Hispanic empire when England had been Spain's most relentless enemy. Ramon y Cajal, himself a great traditionalist, was now to pay his first, his only visit to London, brought there by the tradition of learning. A century after the defeat of the Spanish Armada, a wealthy London physician, Dr. William Croone, had founded one of those charitable trusts that have so astonishing a power of survival. He left money to two most influential learned bodies — the Royal Society and the Royal College of Physicians, charging them to establish an annual lectureship upon 'the advancement of natural knowledge of local motion'. What was 'natural knowledge', and what was 'local motion'? The lawyers of the seventeenth century had no difficulty. Dr. Croone was a man of wide culture. He had lectured upon Rhetoric and Algebra, but he had also lectured on the movement of muscles. The domain of his intellectual interests was quite clear. What is more remarkable is the fact that his definitions had vitality two hundred years after Dr. Croone's death. His words were well able to bear the burden of his testamentary intentions.

In Queen Victoria's reign, 'natural knowledge' had come to mean 'science', and as for Dr. Croone's phrase 'local motion', what could be getter than 'physiology'? It was the Croonian lectureship that brought Ramon y Cajal to England.

He felt a genuine diffidence when the invitation reached him. His innate ambition was always tempered by strong self-criticism. To appear before the Royal Society of London, and to have his Croonian lecture published in its Transactions was to offer himself to the foremost tribunal in the scientific world. True, a minority only of the Fellows were expert histologists; yet experience in one branch of science sharpens the mind towards others, and these men would bring to his paper that cultivated discrimination which an expert enjoys, but fears. Their verdict would be, for the time, absolute. England, moreover, possessed an unusual number of distinguished physiologists. To address them was rather like discoursing on music in Leipzig, or lecturing in Rome upon Canon Law. Ramon y Cajal considered the invitation anxiously, and while he hesitated, one of his daughters took seriously ill. He had now good reason for declining. But Señora Cajal knew her husband, and persuaded him in the direction of his real desires. The family doctor said the child would pull through.

In the summer of 1894, with his discourse carefully translated into French, and microscopic slides in his baggage, Ramon y Cajal arrived in London. His first impressions had astonished him. Looking out of the railway carriage, as he journeyed from Dover until he neared Charing Cross, he saw no great cities, no industries, few factories, fewer people. How could such a country survive? He had been to Germany, and had become aware of the appearance of a modern industrial nation. Now, he felt he had put his finger upon the cause of English decadence. He asked excited questions of his English host, a physiologist five years younger named Charles Scott Sherrington who had visited him in

Valencia some years before. The Englishman only smiled and took the visitor to his house in Battersea. Next day, he would explain.

Dr. Sherrington had a reverence for the doctrine of the neurone, and the rugged simplicity of its author much attracted him. Mrs. Sherrington was surprised at her guest's continental habits. In the morning, she saw the bed linen hanging out of his bedroom window, while the door was locked and the key removed. The Spanish gentleman had in fact behaved as he would have done at home. He had turned the bedroom into a laboratory, and when it was opened, microscopic preparations and lantern slides were found set out all over the furniture and the floor, in a plan corresponding to the theme of the Croonian discourse.

Next morning, Dr. Sherrington took his guest to London Bridge. There, at the start of the working day, thousands were pouring from across the river into the City. Ramon y Cajal was entranced. Here was the feeling of life and activity. Around him he saw business and industry enough to contradict his first impressions of England gained from the countryside. To London Bridge, he insisted upon returning, and withdrew his opinion of English decadence. To his unsophisticated peasant vision, the masses of a city were fascinating raw material. When he went to a shop to buy things, he bargained and chaffered over the price, as though he were in the market square of Huesca. Decidedly, thought Dr. Sherrington's friends, this Spanish guest was an 'original'.

The Croonian lecture of 1894 was considered of more than professional interest, for it received a whole column in the *Illustrated London News*, whose scientific correspondent, Dr. Andrew Wilson, gave an excellent summary. He recorded the essence of Cajal's teaching. Nerve cells were really batteries, and nerve fibres electrical wires. But these cells never increase in number, and after the age of forty, actually decrease. Our real mental power depends more on the richness of cell connections than upon the actual number of these diminishing units, and a fine brain is like a well kept garden, having abundant roots. These ideas must have seemed novel to readers who had no idea of 'local motion' in Dr. Croone's sense. On another page of that issue of the magazine there was a more comprehensible story illustrated by pictures. Wearing an umbrella skirt and pork pie hat, a lady had actually set foot on a battle-ship and inspected the guns and turrets of 'the latest thing on earth'. That was as prophetic of the coming century as was the careful description of Professor Cajal's wires and batteries.

After the Croonian lecture, there was a visit to Cambridge, Dr. Croone's own University, but first of all the Spanish savant paid homage to two other Cambridge graduates who were commemorated in Westminster Abbey. Cajal had a more than Spanish veneration for the past, and in his religion of science there were two great heroes — Isaac Newton and Charles Darwin, to him, much more significant Englishmen than any contemporary figures. They were more characteristic because they were more universal. Less than a century had separated Newton's death from Darwin's birth, and to Cajal Darwin's *The Origin of Species* was a scientific gospel, and its author almost a contemporary. As he paid reverence to the statue of the one and the gravestone of the other, he felt that these two intellectuals represented the rebellion of reason against the power of Churches. From Westminster Abbey he went to Cambridge where these men had been cradled in their faith.

The University was exceptionally rich in physiologists. For thirteen years, the Pope of the science of 'local motion' had been Michael Foster who belonged to Isaac Newton's College. Foster's pupils were now the Cardinals of physiology, for the Pontiff himself had withdrawn from active research. Michael Foster's great gift was his power to inspire others. Having laid hands on a group of able pupils, he himself quitted the physiologist's bench and devoted himself to wider interests — the writing of his great textbook, hybridizing plants in his garden, and later on, being a member of Parliament. But the succession continued in a new and brilliant generation, Walter Holbrook Gaskell, John Newport Langley and others. Nowhere in the world was the study of 'local motion' so ardently pursued as in Cambridge.

Cajal had been so impressed with the importance which the English attached to punctuality, that he took an earlier train than the one intended, and there was no one to meet him at the station. He wandered about in Cambridge entranced by what he saw, and was late for a ceremonial luncheon!

He had come prepared to interchange thoughts in the language of cells and neurones, the speech he understood. He was an artist too, and a connoisseur of old buildings. He walked between the colleges and the river, he saw towers mingled with trees, and lawns bordered by fronts of silver stone. Boys piped in choir stalls beneath perpendicular traceries. Such beauties moved him deeply. Even those ancient stone mantles of Zaragoza and Barcelona appeared mean and jumbled in comparison.

There came the honorary doctorate that is always given to a Croonian lecturer. This was the first of eight occasions when Cajal was to be thus honoured by different Universities. He heard the Orator, describe in Latin his researches into delicate nerve fibres pursuing their inextricable ways, a research based upon an Italian method of silver staining, perfected in Spain. It was very apt and felicitous, thought the guest. These English dons used their Latin as well as their microscopes, though Cambridge pronunciation was not what is current in Latin countries. He was wearing a scarlet gown, and an academic hat 'a pyramidal attachment with a square base'. The son of Don Justo of Ayerbe signed the graduates' roll of Charles Darwin's University.

There was a *conversazione* in the great hall of King's College, an interesting mixture of exact science and social intercourse. One learned don showed his photographs of new stars and planets, another his cultures of microbes. When they had listened to several scientific papers, the audience enjoyed sandwiches and music. It was an eclectic, attractive, and very English affair, as though the universe of contemporary culture were presented upon a Cambridge lawn, and the broad peasant figure in black, with the white beard and Socratic face, put eager questions about physiology, and Cambridge. His notions of English intellectuality were having to be revised.

When Cajal asked about the methods of instruction given in Cambridge he got vague answers. No one here seemed interested in methods. Undergraduates it seemed attended lectures, or stayed away, as it pleased them. In these colleges, there was much culture, but hardly any teaching. The home of Isaac Newton mistrusted intellectual theory. In Cambridge, teachers appeared satisfied when they had turned out an all-round professional man, endowed with handy information. Cajal was a believer in the philosophy of science, and this empirical English attitude seemed lacking in reverence. These friendly persons in blue neckties steered away from general principles, and seemed quite content to follow their inexpressible intuitions. It was to Cajal an unanswerable paradox that men like these had produced highly exact and significant discoveries. Yet general ideas, they seemed to shun, preferring sport, port, and elegant badinage. Cajal concluded that the English had altogether escaped the continental tradition, and that an English University was not a highly geared machine for manufacturing scientists — like Berlin, or Göttingen. In England the man was more important than the organization. Cambridge was an atmosphere, a dream, a beautiful mould, and it aspired to create individuality and character. Those young men, reading as they lay in punts beneath the willows, were the only evidences of any method. Perhaps if Ramon y Cajal had visited Edinburgh, he would have found more respect for general ideas, and Scottish energy and tenacity would have reminded him more of Barcelona.

He returned to London where, to celebrate the Croonian Oration, a banquet was given by the Royal Society. To Cajal, it was a more entertaining and less rigid affair than a similar banquet would have been in Madrid. Michael Foster praised the guest in a witty speech that would not have been out of place at the *Café Suizo*. Ramon y Cajal he said, had found the brain

an impenetrable forest, but had turned it into a delightful
park. The Croonian lecture, he declared, had an
international significance. It had brought together
England and Spain, two nations separated previously
by centuries of misunderstanding. An English after
dinner speech, which could be urbane and amusing,
mixing fact with grace, appealed to the guest who was
not used to such unbending on a serious occasion. There
was a party at the Spanish Embassy, where his Hispanic
Majesty's representative Don Cipriano de Mazo proposed his health and said that in all the experiences of
his life, three had impressed him most: they were Niagara
Falls, the Coliseum at Rome and the Croonian lecture.
Ramon y Cajal listened with pleasure. Ah, here was
rhetoric, here was the true Latin sense of drama and
exuberance. His Excellency's toast must have been
more congenial to Cajal than those English frivolities.
He was Niagara, he was the Coliseum — grotesque
figures of speech perhaps — yet how sweet to hear such
phrases in the Spanish tongue after those years of
indifference at home.

He returned to Madrid and was delighted to find his
daughter recovered, and when he unpacked the toys he
had brought from London, he found that even this had
been anticipated by his friends who had lavished gifts
upon the children of an absent physiologist.

Even the austere monotony of the Spanish landscape
charmed his eye. It was such a contrast to the over-lush
northern countries, where, it seemed to him, the excessive greenness demanded the colour sense of a cater-
pillar. In Spain his feelings were satisfied by the
penetrating poetry of grey, orange and ochre, under a
flawless blue sky.

CHAPTER XXIX

SATISFACTIONS AT HOME

IT was depressing to look around his own University when memories of the trees and colleges of Cambridge were fresh in his mind. In Madrid, the meanness of the academic buildings, the wretched lodgings where the students lived, the general lack of a corporate spirit — external features they seemed, of an inward indifference, drove him deeper into his own work in the private laboratory which Don Busto's bounty had helped to provide. The University of which he was a professor did not inspire him, and he was thrown further into his personal achievements. He was beginning to find satisfaction in what he had accomplished, after so many years of labour.

Ten years at the microscope had produced eighty scientific papers and two books. In the trackless brain forest, he had learned to find his way. Concentration had given him self-confidence, although he was continually challenged by disconcerting novelties. The brain was a world of its own, and a law unto itself. So diverse were the patterns of its tissue architecture that he was frequently thrown back in wonderment and doubt. He compared his conclusions as between man and animals. Nerve ganglions of a squid, the *axon* terminations in a dove, the *thalamus* of a rabbit — each made its contribution to the complete architectural scheme. It was not enough merely to describe a particular organ — he wished to account for its place in the devious path of evolution. The background, the analogies, the dissimilarities of each tissue had to be accounted for by his own exhaustive methods. The mechanical handling of dead and stained material was in itself a problem. Who could be certain that those elements which looked so convincing were really the truth, or only some aberration of technique?

Admittedly, the histologist could no more cause a nerve process to disappear than an astronomer could eliminate a fixed star. Yet the truth of tissue observation depended largely upon his choice of a sound method, and even then, there were difficulties of interpretation. The histologist's eye did not always see what was there, and would sometimes experience an illusion.

Golgi's method of staining caused a sheath of metallic silver to be thrown around the nerve elements, so that they appeared dark brown, or black. Some types of tissue were thereby rendered bold and clear. Sometimes, it was just the reverse. For instance, in the *medulla oblongata* (a mass of nerve centres at the base of the brain), the slide would reveal a wearisome thicket of cells, although in that bewildering labyrinth, the histologist would occasionally find a flower of rare beauty. As Cajal sketched those outlines, critical doubts came over his mind. Some histologists asserted that those dark lines and brown curves were not nerve elements at all, but merely streaks of silver stain which had stuck in the preparation. At such large magnification a big error was always possible. Though not accepting the criticism, he was obliged to go over his work many times. Instead of growing simpler, his field had become more complex. Each fresh tissue caused him to question previous assumptions. Separate parts of the brain had been descriptively labelled by the old anatomists; there was the *pons* or bridge, which connected two halves of the brain together; the *hippocampus* — named because it resembled the sea-horse; the *thalamus*, after a Greek word for a couch. Their general relationship was clear. But when one came to examine these structures under the microscope, each was found to be made up of cells so fantastically different that generalization seemed impossible.

Such wrestling with the infinitesimal became wearisome unless one could rise above it. How could he answer insistent questions — how all this came to be, and what future it foretold? Cajal would leave his working bench, and go to the *Café Suizo* to find relaxation in talk. Some argued that the Fathers of the Church had said the last word upon all problems of human destiny and free will. But orthodoxy had upon the mature Cajal the same effect as those impassioned lectures of Don Vicente Ventura exercised when the school boy of Huesca. To his friends, Don Santiago was a confirmed rationalist. In this mood he would return to his microscopic preparations, searching in that natural architecture for some natural explanation. If the human brain were really man's organ of destiny, must not the key to the human enigma lie somewhere in those tiny cells? Actual observations gave him little help. He was obliged to conclude that the cells within the brain were just as unpredictable as the human being as a whole. Yet, the unbelievable variety of those neurones, their power of responding so faithfully to external environment, might not those qualities be the basis of free will? Man has always yearned for an explanation of the unknown. The human spirit finds it hard to bear the suspense and incertitude of its own limited powers. He needed a theory to explain how brain had evolved through thousands of human generations out of millions of pre-human forms, a theory to fit his laboriously acquired facts, yet capable of leading him towards the future evolution of this fascinating cerebral organ. One of the good things of growing experience was that Cajal began to feel a satisfaction finer than that of mere technical accomplishment. There came the delight of a provisional philosophy, which was not discordant with fact.

There is the so-called 'lower', or unconscious nerve mechanism, made up of trunks like the Sympathetic, which works day and night, like an automatic telephone exchange, and controls such functions as breathing and digestion, which it would be highly inconvenient to have to remember every time they are needed. This 'automatic' nervous system is much the same in animals as in man. It progresses only by growing more intricate. Otherwise, it has completed its story.

Aeons later there had developed the 'higher' nervous system belonging to the brain proper, with its incredibly varied architecture. Its cells are much more numerous, their connections more complex. Cajal's friend in Cambridge, Charles Scott Sherrington called the brain 'an enchanted loom where millions of flashing shuttles weave a dissolving pattern'. It is the brain's complexity which has given mankind the power to think and to will. Those powers are due to the variety of those neurones which had almost defeated Cajal. His observation that evolution seems to contradict itself in each tissue was confirmed by the infinite flexibility of the brain's functions. Unlike the 'lower' nervous system, its story was by no means finished. Cajal had been led to this fundamental understanding through the very magnitude of his doubts. Any sort of simplification would carry him away from the truth. Yet something was gained, if one kept near observed facts. His philosophy of living things liberated him from the microscopic world. Those paraffin sections were minute, but they raised the mind to cosmic issues.

In his early career, Cajal had been compelled to translate his papers into French or German, since few histologists bothered to learn Spanish. Now, the case was different. His own work had become significant enough to induce foreigners to read what he had to say in his own language. He founded his own quarterly journal, the *Revista Trimestral Micrographica*, of which the first number, appearing in 1896, contained seven papers, written and illustrated by himself. Even at this date, the plates were simple when compared with his later efforts. Further issues contained articles by other members of the Spanish school of histology which was being formed in Madrid under his personal leadership. Among his followers was one unexpected person — no other than Don Justo's second son, the unsatisfactory Pedro, who for ten years had been lost in the wilderness of Paraguay. He had not only survived but had prospered, returning to Spain and becoming qualified in medicine. His elder brother's success inspired Pedro, who took up histology, and after surmounting the *oposiciones* became Professor in the University of Cadiz. His researches into marine biology brought him frequently into the pages of the *Revista Trimestral*. Pedro's appetite for adventure had been completely satisfied by his ten years among the *Indios*, and he never achieved that perfect transmutation of romance into scientific achievement that made his brother Santiago unique.

One day, a professor of the University of Madrid happened to be in Berlin, talking to Rudolf Virchow, the greatest man in continental medicine, and the German savant who knew everyone worth knowing, inquired after Ramon y Cajal. The Spanish professor was obliged to confess he did not know the name. Home in Madrid, he made inquiries, and so influential was even a word from the great Virchow when whispered to the Royal Academy of Madrid, that Cajal was elected a member. He was also made a correspondent of learned societies in Paris, Vienna and Lisbon. He became an honorary doctor of the University of Wurzburg. At last in 1897 came his great textbook on the *Texture of the Nervous System in Man and Vertebrates*, with 567 pages, and 206 plates in monochrome and colour. It was awarded a prize of a thousand pesetas and a further thousand francs from Paris. This was only the first volume, and seven years passed before the work was complete.

It was as though all those separate instincts of his — to use his hands, to draw pictures, to philosophize — were behaving like those individualistic neurones in the brain. Each struggled to find a termination. Each cross-communicated with others. And they had succeeded in their disparate aims. Who could have planned such a career, through drawing, to histology, and by its discipline, to a philosophy of the brain? Cajal was the natural child of adversity. No different method of education could have produced a finer result.

There is, however, one positive clue that illuminates his success. Ramon y Cajal was congenitally fortunate in his sanguine temperament. His melancholy was deep, but it never lasted. The shadows of boyhood had not spoiled his power to enjoy. Sometimes, in the laboratory, he would meditate upon death, though not in the Spanish fashion of dread of personal dissolution. His philosophy lifted him above the narrow issue of personal destiny. It made him contemplate the cosmic suicide which all life on the earth seemed fated to undergo, and which one day would mean extinction. If such were the final judgment of science upon the human situation, what use was it to labour? Why strive against inevitable annihilation? He looked out of the window. The Sunday crowd was on its way to the bullfight — handsome men storming the coaches, pretty women, courting couples, children, eager, self-confident representatives of life's powerful exuberance. The pessimistic hermit of the laboratory felt himself carried along by their unconquerable spirit. In such eager vitality, the primary forces of nature possessed a justification which was hidden even from the student of brain cells. Such a swing from the gloom of theory to the delight of experience was characteristic of Cajal. No religion of science ever absorbed his eager vitality.

Just about these years, another great natural philosopher, who had similar preoccupation with a very small world was living and working in the South of France. He was Jean Henri Fabre, an ageing teacher in a village near Orange. He devoted superhuman patience to study the world of insects. No one has ever described so subtly the behaviour of mason bees, the spiders, cicadas, wasps and caterpillars. With home-made apparatus, he carried out his experiments in his own garden. With tribulation he published his papers. With the exception of Charles Darwin, few scientists paid much heed to the obscure schoolmaster, he was given no grants for study, no prizes, not even an honorary degree. He longed not for fame, but for a little leisure, and extra money for more apparatus. It never came, not to the end. Yet in time, his writings spread all over the world. Fabre achieved only one of his worldly ambitions, and that when he was very old. He managed to buy a small piece of land where he could devote himself undisturbed to the insects.

How different is that soured, unprosperous life from the career of Ramon y Cajal. And the source of the difference lies in temperament.

CHAPTER XXX

INTELLECTUAL RENAISSANCE

IN the century which followed Christopher Columbus, the Spanish empire included the whole of South America (except Brazil), and a large slice of North America as well, extending in fact from Cape Horn to San Francisco. There were also the Philippines, the West Indies, and possessions in Africa — all this, in addition to the Emperor's domains in Germany and Flanders.[1] Then in less than two centuries, this gigantic overseas *imperium* melted away. The great provinces of Latin America became independent States — Argentine, Peru, Chile and others. New Mexico, Texas, Arizona passed to France, and then by purchase to the U.S.A. There remained now only those Caribbean islands which Columbus had first explored, and the Philippines on the other side of the world.

When Cuba revolted in 1872, Ramon y Cajal had his only taste of tropical life, and suffered the personal misfortunes that led him so oddly into a career of science. Now once more in 1898, there was a sudden explosion. A brief war with the United States, ended in the humiliating defeat of Spain. The New World conquests of Columbus, of Pizarro and Cortés, of Charles V and Phillip II had become no more than history. Such memories had left their influence on the Spanish soul. Greater even than what remained — the Canary Islands and some unproductive territory in Africa — was the profound psychological and racial tradition.

[1] Also large areas of Italy.

The historical event of 1898 is not irrelevant to the career of a man of science. One day, science may become truly international, as theology was once. If ever local loyalties become merged into one supranational organization of the intellectual life, it may be that the influences in a man that spring from a particular region of earth, and a special mixture of heredity, will have no significance. This has not yet come to pass. Ramon y Cajal, even when in Paris or London, could never be anything but a proud Spaniard. His patriotism went back to childhood, when they roasted the ox in the Square at Valpalmas. While demonstrating a microscopic slide in Berlin, he was really asserting Spain's scientific capacity. He desired to win for his country a more enduring intellectual empire.

The intellectuals of Madrid awoke to what had been lost through the Spanish-American War. It was more than rich territory, it was honour. The peasant sons of Spain had gone forth and created twenty nations. Language, religion, customs, architecture had blossomed over an enormous area of land and sea. Such things could never be taken away. Now the empire had gone and culture was all that remained. Those talkers in cafés in the *Calle de Alcala* who felt most bitterly this humiliation, and struggled to eliminate its causes, were called 'the men of '98'. They formed a definite group of impatient men with a distinctive point of view, and prominent among them was Ramon y Cajal.

He understood, more inwardly than many others, why Spanish colonialism had failed. Malaria, yellow fever, were prime causes of deterioration, and the inertia of officialdom was a disease in itself. The seventeenth century, the age of gold, had no chance against the nineteenth, the age of iron. Seventeen million Spaniards could not oppose ninety million Americans. How did Spain's ancient enemies England and Holland manage to hold to their colonies? Through a spirit of adaptation which Spain lacked. Cajal, a fervent admirer of the modern Germany, drew a contrast between the discipline of the Germans, and the ferocious individualism of his own people. Yet — it was a paradox, those docile Teutons had originated great religious and philosophical changes, whilst Spain, where every man considered himself unique, lived by flattering her Church, her Kings and her rich men. Over the coffee cups of the *Café Suizo* Don Santiago analysed Spanish decadence with sombre rhetoric. Small piles of bread crumbs were discharged at his opponents. His large magnetic eyes made them diffident.

He did not spare the failings of his own countrymen: their irresistible habit of solving problems by killing off a few thousand fellow Spaniards in a stubborn civil war; their traditions which had hardened into an obsession. Philip II had governed his world-wide empire from his combined study and bedchamber in the Escorial, where he could stare at the High Altar through a casement. From this had developed the fixed idea that all Spanish administration must be centralized, and influenced by the Church. Over the centuries of her decline, inertia and resignation had come to be the marks of Hispanic thought. Ramon y Cajal resolved to change all this.

His renaissance was to come from science.

He aspired to rejuvenate his country not by killing men, but by destroying ideas. Spain, known as the land of beggars and castanets, must turn her energies into scientific achievements. He prepared to exploit his own prestige abroad, for he knew the sycophantic custom in Spain was to ignore what was original at home, and greet it with excessive praise when it came from outside. He attacked Spanish degeneration with his microscope, and with that personal renown that the neurone doctrine had brought him. He called for a reform of education, demanded less imitation, less borrowing, less secondhand culture.

It was indeed an enterprise worthy of Don Quixote. Yet Spain has always had her visionaries.

Among the men of '98 was a professor, a short person with twinkling eyes and a pointed beard, named Francisco Giner de los Rios who looked, in his black robe, like a figure in El Greco. His subject in the University was the philosophy of law, but that was merely an excuse for brilliant exposition over a wide range. Ramon y Cajal sometimes went to his lectures, out of friendship and sympathy for his ideas for no one knew what Giner would say next. He disdained notes, never bothered to record attendance, and held no examinations. One day, in the middle of his discourse, he halted, confessed the subject was beyond him, and came to a stop. Upon receptive minds he had a profound spell. Giner de los Rios was the ideal professor — for the ideal student. He was really interested only in one theme, the art of influencing minds. He set up a society for 'free education' which had ideas much in advance of its age, and methods somewhat like those of Montessori and Patrick Geddes. It disfavoured reliance on textbooks, and encouraged visits to factories, museums and historic places. Above all, the Professor advised study tours in foreign countries.

It was this idea which most appealed to Ramon y Cajal. To dispatch gifted students outside Spain, that was the way to revolutionize Spanish education. To Cajal, it meant sending abroad his more gifted pupils for a semester in a German or French laboratory or a *wanderjahr* like these diligent Teutons. If only in those formative years when he laboured with the microscope, having no teacher but a meagre French textbook, he himself had been given the chance to study abroad under a man like Wilhelm Krause of Göttingen, or Van Gehuchten of Louvain. Cajal had the self-educated man's desire to give instruction to others. He favoured taking the elementary schools out of the hands of monks and nuns — like those Aesculapian Fathers who had taught him in Jaca. He would have liked to remodel the Universities upon German lines.

Education in Spain was an ancient structure with massive foundations and heavy walls, full of gloomy chambers dating back to the remote past. There was a tendency to say of any new idea that it had already been tried in the seventeenth century and failed. It was not till 1907, under a short-lived Liberal Ministry, that Ramon y Cajal had any opportunity of personal influence upon education.

That opportunity, he declined, as will be described presently.

But fate gave him a second chance. He was appointed Chairman of a Board — a *junta*, for widening the scope of education by sending exceptional students abroad. It was called *Junta para Ampliacion de los Estudios*, and it drew a subsidy from the Government. Its twenty-one life members, drawn from different Faculties. Medicine was represented by Cajal's old friend, Don Luis Simarro of Valencia, but as chairman Cajal possessed the biggest influence.

In practice, the *junta* managed to reconcile men of extreme views in different intellectual camps. It began by sending students abroad for post-graduate study, with travelling fellowships. The Government had first attempted to restrict the subjects chosen for study, but the *junta* resisted such pressure, and the scholar was allowed to select his own course of study and choose the foreign University he preferred. They were appointed after personal interview, and were sometimes required to undertake a preliminary period of research in Spain before they were considered worthy of a foreign tour. In the later period of its existence, the *junta* established institutes and colleges inside Spain. For thirty years, the *junta* for amplifying Spanish studies remained a vital force. It was called 'a vaccine injected into the official mind of Spain'. The *junta* passed through many political vicissitudes. At one critical moment, its adroit secretary only saved its life against a Ministerial onslaught by pouring ridicule upon it, and falsely pretending that it did nothing but provide a dole for a few pensioners. Even the dictator Primo de Rivera did not manage to bring it to an end.

The *junta* was never really popular with the Spanish Universities. It was too free, too experimental, and it favoured science. Ramon y Cajal and his colleagues were under suspicion from the religious authorities which ruled education and who were correct in thinking that these men might be Catholics, but were certainly anticlerical. Don Francisco Giner, their original inspirer, had himself fallen under official opprobrium. One day, at a period much earlier, some Civil Guards had appeared at his home, requesting the Señor Professor to accompany them to Cadiz — which as everyone knew, was the place of embarkation for the Canary Islands, a notorious seat of exile for Spanish intellectuals. The powers had relented, and he got no further than Cadiz. But the fact remained a shadow across the path of liberal ideas.

The *junta* for the amplification of studies owed its success mainly to Ramon y Cajal, yet it never completely realized his own visions. Like some cathedral of the sierras, of grandiose design but with an unfinished tower, it remained a memorial to the spirit of the men of '98.

This is to anticipate, and to carry Cajal's educational projects beyond the original impulse which created them out of the pessimism following the Spanish-American War. For the time, that national humiliation paralysed his power to work. He could not bring himself even to look down a microscope. His mind was preoccupied with politics. He could not unbend it upon sections. In the café, he heard nothing but rhetorical outpourings. But rhetoric, he bitterly reflected, was merely the fringe, the surface, and had no power to arrest national decadence.

The war and its disastrous ending had in fact interrupted a piece of research that called up his deepest emotion. It was the study of the mechanism of vision.

Ramon y Cajal was one of the great visuals, who live through their eyes, and are so specialized in that faculty as to be capable of observing the depths, when others see only the surface. Man's visual faculty was the basis of what appealed most to Cajal — art and photography. In his usual exhaustive fashion, he attacked this visual apparatus — both in man and animals. He was to find it the most complex theme in histology.

We think we 'see' with the eyes, but this is merely an

approximation. The eye is merely the passive receiver. It does no more than accept a flash of light which is then conveyed to the 'visual' area of the cortex at the back of the brain by means of optic nerve fibres which emerge from the rear of each eyeball. What is unexpected about these optic nerve fibres is that some of them cross over from right to left and vice versa. If this crossing did not occur, it would mean that the picture taken by each eye would remain separate. Nature had to invent a method by which the images from both eyes became fused together, like the twin pictures in an old-fashioned stereoscope, or a modern multi-dimensional cinema film. This combining of the two images is made possible by the crossing of the fibres. In due course, the brain blends those images together, and what we 'see' is a fusion of both. Such is 'binocular vision' a much richer power of seeing than that possible with one eye alone, as any person who has lost one eye discovers.

The 'crossing' of the optic nerve fibres takes place in the way in which the reins from a pair of horses cross into the hands of the driver, so that his right hand controls the right side of both horses, and his left hand both left sides. Thus, the brain receives an image simultaneously from the right half of both right and left eyes.

This 'crossing' of nerve fibres had long been an accepted fact of histology, but suddenly, it was challenged and by no less a person than the great Albert von Kölliker of the University of Wurzburg. Cajal was roused out of his depression which had cursed him since the Spanish-American War. To abandon the beautiful theory of 'binocular' vision — it was too great a sacrifice. Even von Kölliker could not be allowed to destroy this fundamental of the biologist's faith, at least not without a struggle. The challenge renewed Cajal's belief in the power of work. He ceased to think of a lost Spanish empire, and dreamed of conquests to come.

It was easy to find suitable specimens of the visual apparatus in amphibians, insects, birds — to form the basis of this campaign against Kölliker, but not so convenient to obtain human specimens, especially at the embryonic stage which would reveal the optic fibres in their early growth. Spanish law prohibited a post-mortem examination until at least twenty-four hours after death. Such delay defeated Cajal's purpose, since the fragile tissues of the nervous system are the earliest to suffer loss of vitality. A section made on the second day showed nothing but dead fibres.

Here was an occasion for the Robinson Crusoe faculty. He discovered that in the Foundling Hospital the law about post mortems was respected, but not observed. Not all members of religious orders were enemies of science. Here there was a friendly Sister who helped him, and he was able to get delicate sections of the human visual tract, at an early stage of development. That episode in the Foundling Hospital recalls Don Justo taking bones from the churchyard. Biologists in search of material had to make their own rules.

Cajal's comprehensive studies of the visual apparatus were published in several articles at the end of the century and enabled physiology to resume her progress. He showed that the earlier view of the 'crossing' of optic fibres had been correct, and the great von Kölliker had been wrong. Fibres from each eye divide in the centre, so that both halves of the brain participate in the work of both eyes. The progress of a science is full of such retraced paths and seemingly wasted efforts, but now it was proof of the prestige that Ramon y Cajal had attained that his refutation of von Kölliker should have been accepted as a pronouncement carrying final authority. Such researches restored his faith, and enabled him to forget the muddling of politicians. The Spanish Church and the Monarchy sometimes made him despair, but he believed in the neurones, with a fervour like that of the little boy who timed the solar eclipse with his father's watch.

That boy of Valpalmas was now turned fifty. His beard was white, and those large and luminous eyes were coming to have the venerable look of a Greek philosopher in marble. In his long maturing, he seemed to grow younger, and more wide-minded. His acquired expertness in the tedious routine of histology set his mind free for larger things, and overcame the temptation of a specialist to hide in his own technique. The boyhood vision of Robinson Crusoe, became not weaker but stronger, the imaginary island grew more vivid.

CHAPTER XXXI

A SPANIARD DISCOVERS THE NEW WORLD

T HE old, the nineteenth century was nearing its end, and the men of Ramon y Cajal's generation fervently looked to the coming age as one destined to be great through science. Prophets predicted its marvels with the assurance of men two thousand years earlier who prophesied the millennium within a human lifetime. Once those unfathomable technical resources were employed for the benefit of mankind, no one doubted a second coming of peace and happiness.

To most Europeans, the home of this modern spirit was the United States of America and one day in Madrid, Ramon y Cajal received a letter that confirmed a natural incredulity towards its fantastic possibilities. The President of Clark University, Worcester, Massachusetts, had invited him to cross the Atlantic and deliver six lectures on the function of the brain cortex. Cajal could not believe so astonishing a proposal. His patriotism was wounded and still raw. Only a year before, Spain had been grossly insulted, defeated, robbed of her last New World colony. How could a victorious nation wish to show honour to the representative of a vanquished people? Did these Americans desire to hold him to mockery? It seemed dishonourable to entertain such an invitation, or think of accepting the six hundred dollars offered for the cost of the journey. The newspapers of Madrid still published columns of ferocious abuse of the *Americanos*. Yet those greedy imperialists, who by trickery, propaganda and physical force had despoiled his country were now expecting him to meet them. His Spanish dignity was outraged.

How could he properly realize the immense generosity, tolerance and indifference of America? How could a Latin mind, at that date, conceive of the American people's astonishing power of effacing the past and embracing the future? The authorities of Clark University were not in the least bothered by any hostile feelings towards Spain. To them, any such idea if it could have entered their heads, was irrelevant to the grand object, that of celebrating the tenth anniversary of the founding of Clark. They wanted to bring the best authorities in Europe. Ramon y Cajal was the greatest name in brain physiology. That was good enough for Clark — be he Spaniard or Hottentot.

To Cajal's great surprise, the Faculty of the University of Madrid favoured his acceptance, and Señora Cajal was ready to make the journey. Everything conspired to draw him again across the Atlantic, thirty years after his first unpleasant taste of the New World.

They sailed, after a short visit to Paris, from Le Havre, and it was twelve days before they reached the Ambrose Light. On the same liner were two other visitors to Clark University, equally surprised by this invitation. There was Auguste Forel a Swiss naturalist, who had brought a paper on the behaviour of ants, and Angelo Mosso of the University of Turin whose investigation into the physiology of muscle action was well known. The decennial celebrations at Clark were strongly flavoured by the physiology of the nervous system owing to the bias of its President Granville Stanley Hall, who was an educational pioneer with a European training in those sciences. The tide of knowledge was still flowing from

East to West. However great her future potentialities, America was yet immature in science, and thirsty for enlightenment that only the old world could give. These European scholars felt like missionaries of a scientific culture.

New York offered the first of a series of shocks. Madrid in summer is hot enough, but the heat of America was appalling. Ramon y Cajal, who felt uncomfortable at home when the thermometer touched 80°, was now prostrated by temperature that went up to 90° in his hotel apartment, and 113° outside and the humidity was more trying than anything encountered in arid Spain. No sooner were they safely inside the apartment, high up in a skyscraper, when a fire alarm sounded on a lower floor, and they had the first experience of panic. Everyone rushed to the main staircase, but Cajal more coolly conducted his wife to an emergency exit, where he had great difficulty in persuading her to descend those horribly exposed ironwork steps against the side of the building. Afterwards when they were on ground level, and the fire had turned out to be less dangerous than the excitement, he philosophized upon the effect of sudden fear in bringing out instinctive actions — such as flight from danger — that would normally not be noticed.

As he became more accustomed to the mighty city, Cajal became less and less at ease over his wife. He was continually trying to safeguard her, and naturally she accepted his tutelage 'like a good Spanish woman'. But these Americans cared nothing for the European convention that a wife's personality was merged in her husband. Newspaperwomen were continually putting questions to the Señora. Her husband was continually rushing in to protect her. As she saw his masculine efforts, she became all the more timid, but the intense curiosity of journalism never slackened. Reporters seemed to wish to hear what Señora Cajal thought — from her own lips — instead of from her husband's proprietary explanations. To him, it was extraordinary, it was unchivalrous! He was none the less fascinated by the stores of Broadway and Fifth Avenue, especially by those ingenious electric railways by which their change was conveyed to customers. Everywhere he used his camera to capture the colossal realities of New York, its canyons of streets, its vibrating crowds, and horse omnibuses. He ran into parties of Spanish-speaking refugees who had escaped from Cuba. Their horror stories of camps and cruelties brought back all his mistrust of American imperialism. Yet, here he was, in the middle of New York, a half-willing, half-compulsory victim of American zeal for the learning he had gathered in thirty years.

American efficiency had not yet learned to condition the atmosphere, and after a stifling railroad journey of several hours, he reached the city of Worcester, and went to bed. Next morning, he was awakened by pandemonium below his windows, worse even than the uproar in the Madrid bull-ring when the matador has angered the crowd. These Americans were shouting like madmen, actually firing off rifles in the street. Surely, an insurrection had broken out against President Cleveland! All Cajal's Latin horror of these inexplicable people came back. He was nervous for Señora Cajal, remembering those Carlist wars in the days of his youth. But this was not a revolutionary outbreak. The citizens of Worcester, Mass., were merely celebrating the Fourth of July.

The Professor who arrived to conduct them to meet

their host had two characteristics quite unusual in the European professoriate: he was young, and he was smartly dressed. After ceremonious greetings, Ramon y Cajal called for a porter to deal with their luggage, but while they waited, the young American behaved with sudden eccentricity. He actually seized the bags, and without any assistance soon had them on the top of the cab. The Señor and Señora were astonished. They thought of his professorial dignity, and those immaculate clothes. Politely, they demurred; surely that was what the hotel porter was for. This gave the Professor an opening for a lecture. He addressed these benighted Europeans on the true meaning of democracy. America, sir, was a land where manual labour was not despised, where every man was equal, where the only aristocracy lay in talent and learning. They had the next surprise on meeting an amiable bachelor, Mr. Stephen Salisbury, who was their host, and who greeted them with his few words of Spanish. He had been a great benefactor to Clark University, and he never wearied of talking — about himself, and his gifts to Clark, past and future. Naturally, he told them, he was a Protestant and a free-thinker. What kept him unmarried was his abhorrence of American femininity. 'You, Professor, are a man of common sense, sir, but in Spain, the women are more talented than the men.' He bowed to the Señora. Ramon y Cajal was puzzled. It was not long before he sensed that Americans had nothing but scorn for the peoples of Southern Europe, who held on to their decadent way of life, instead of emulating America and embracing the benefits of democracy and commerce. In his loud agree-able tones, Mr. Salisbury aired his views, poured forth wisecracks, denounced everything, even his own country.

Then it dawned upon Cajal that their host loved the sound of his own voice, and that his opinions were not all to be taken at face value or in their literal meaning. In America, eccentricity was admired, and no one ever bothered to stop talking. He was told something of the background of Clark College. It was only ten years old.

A self-made New Englander, Jonas G. Clark had been a prosperous carriage builder, who went west and made an even larger fortune in California. He had the plain man's superstitious belief in education. He retired home to his native city of Worcester. Looking round for a President for his proposed College, he found a young teacher called Granville Stanley Hall, a *Mayflower* descendant. He too was a self-educated man, though in a different sense from the founder of Clark. Hall was indeed a man of omnivorous intellectual appetite, devoted to philosophy who was also a man of determination. As a pupil teacher, he had thrashed a surly boy for chewing tobacco in class. He began to study theology, but diverged into philosophy, and went for two years to Germany where modern psychology was being born. Back home in the States, he was ordained Minister, then took teaching posts at Harvard and Johns Hopkins. In 1889, he was chosen by the shrewd founder of Clark, and there opened the ten years of hard-fisted patronage, varied by periods of acute controversy. The patron wished to concentrate upon undergraduates, believing that the benefits of education should be widely dispersed. The president favoured a post-graduate institution. The one had the money; the other his passionate belief in higher education. At the ten year celebrations, the battle was in its closing stages. A year after Cajal's visit, Jonas Clark died, and attained his final victory from beyond the grave. He willed his fortune to the undergraduate college.

Academic politics in the New World were decidedly not simple. They had been invited to Clark as ornaments for the President's chariot. Those visitors from Switzerland, Italy and Spain perhaps only dimly comprehended this academic conflict, but their presence was a tribute to the President's discernment. Granville Stanley Hall had faith in the future of the mental sciences and a few years later, he was to bring Sigmund Freud to Clark.

Cajal had originally intended his lectures to cover the whole of the brain cortex, but that proved too ambitious, even for six discourses. So he restricted himself to his favourite subject, the visual connections of the brain, and he illustrated the theme in his usual thorough way, with drawings and lantern slides. The lectures were a great success.

Mr. Stephen Salisbury gave a party at the Quinsigamond boat club, and there was the inevitable honorary degree. Ramon y Cajal became a graduate of Clark. His speech of acceptance reveals his personal creed when he was at the height of his powers. It throws a light upon the ethical pretensions of a scientist at the start of the twentieth century. Science, said Cajal, was superior to the wrangle of material interests and the selfish struggle of nationalities. All industrial progress had its birth in some original scientific discovery, and a great nation must attend to the laboratory as much as the mill. This happy alliance between science and practice had placed Germany at the head of civilization. German aniline chemistry, German optical industry (sprung from the labours of scientists) 'by their manifest superiority over that of other nations procures Prussia a monopoly which makes the whole world her tributary'. This was the right way, he said, the only way that led to glory, wealth and power. He expressed the hope that 'the creation of Clark University would be the signal for founding in America similar institutions embracing a larger number of branches of science, having their primary object the wresting of secrets from nature, supplying industry and arts with principles and facts capable of fruitful application, forming the research spirit of the new generation, freeing it from the clogs of routine, and making finally the foundation of a splendid civilization superior in groundwork as well as in form to that of the European nations'. The applause was very loud.

Had Ramon y Cajal succumbed to the exuberant American air? Was this the real opinion of a man of European culture? The frank materialism of this speech, replacing his bitter sentiments towards America of only a year before, reflected so well the authentic note of the New World, and the echo of the frontier. What Cajal praised in that rhetorical worship of wealth and power has since come to pass. Today, the lesson of scientific application is the lesson which America teaches Europe. That advice which Cajal gave at the tenth anniversary of Clark is one which has been well learned by American colleges, and now followed half unwillingly by the rest of the world. In this, Ramon y Cajal was a prophet. Praise of Germany had been frequent on his lips ever since his first triumphs in Berlin. The Catalan spirit of efficiency fitted this scientific gospel. Jena and Heidelberg were to be the models for the future. This was a message likely to appeal strongly to New Englanders such as Stephen Salisbury and President Stanley Hall.

Ramon y Cajal possessed a disconcerting artistic sympathy which enabled him to divine the mood of a foreign country— in England the ethical basis of her academic culture, in Germany her technique, and now in the U.S.A. this reverence for material progress. He found it impossible not to be captivated by the warmth and vitality of Americans. He was even persuaded to throw back towards Europe that same half-disapproving, patronizing look which he had caught from the drawling witticisms of Mr. Stephen Salisbury. Suddenly, the mood changed. Cajal became a Spaniard once more.

Newspapermen had demanded his opinions upon the late Spanish-American War. Cajal felt all his Hispanic instincts return. He drew himself up with the pride of an *hidalgo*. It was shocking even to mention such a question here in a land where he was a guest. To a Spaniard it was like discussing ropes when a man had just been hanged. The American reporters had no sympathy with such inhibitions, and pressed on him further questions about the war and the peace. To them, the more indiscreet his replies, the better. Then Ramon y Cajal delivered a serious and considered opinion. To him, it was a matter of honour, something to be gravely answered. He was horrified to read in the newspapers what he was supposed to have said, and find the tone of his judicial opinions transmuted into something quite American. He regretted that he had given an answer at all. Female reporters were still pertinacious in demanding the views of Señora Cajal. Again and again her husband rushed in to protect her, with the heroic words: 'Madam, our Spanish women are backward, they are happy in the home, they are content to be feminine without being feminist.' It was a speech worthy of Don Quixote de la Mancha. The newspaperwomen recorded a fresh instance of European backwardness.

CHAPTER XXXII

CROSS OF ISABEL THE CATHOLIC

AFTER a first experience of America, no European is quite the same. Returning to Spain after the mental intensity of the New World gave Cajal that abrupt sense of strain which is caused by a sudden shutting off of exuberance. For the time, the slower rhythm is more fatiguing than previous excitement. In Latin countries, men allow themselves to age more quickly than in ever-young America. Cajal felt himself getting old. He began to have heart attacks, and to feel a need for air and space. Though he was no more than fifty, he felt that old age had gained upon him.

On the outskirts of Madrid he found a village at a crossroads — it was named Quatro Caminos, a place where peasants and labourers lived. Here was a small house, with an incomparable view. He moved out of the city, and found that sense of free air for which he hungered. On the one side, he could observe the village people — the men singing as they issued from the *pulqueria*, and the women dressed up to go to Mass. In the other direction, there was the long blue line of the Guadarrama, rising majestic and bare to seven thousand feet. Their snow-covered faces gave him the mountain smell he remembered from the Pyrenees when he was a boy. In the distance could be seen the great grey pile of the Escorial. He realized after all he was not old. That supposed malady of the cardiac organ was an illusion bred in a closed city. In the country, under trees and in sight of the mountains, his heart attacks ceased, while his native optimism and power of work returned. There was a small garden where he kept the guinea-pigs and rabbits whose tissues would presently come under his microscope. Cajal had his own vines, olives, spread out on rising ground. He had now a retreat from the world.

No sooner was he installed in this pleasant hermitage than Spaniards awoke to the greatness of Ramon y Cajal, and overwhelmed him with belated appreciation. For years, in Valencia, in Zaragoza he had worked like a mole in obscurity; now, everyone wished to praise him. Cynically, he told himself that such an outburst of glory meant nothing more than a brief postponement of inevitable oblivion. 'When I clapped for the waiter in the café, the wretched pianist thought I was applauding him.' At one time, Spain had never heard of him. Now, his country had taken notice. It was no more than that.

An international conference held in Moscow had devoted its superfluous funds to founding a prize to be awarded for the best medical or biological work in the previous three years. Ramon y Cajal received six thousand francs. The King sent him a message, and invested him with the Grand Cross of the Order of Isabel the Catholic — that creator of modern Spain, whose pious example of unification had been so little to the taste of Catalonians.

During his eighty-three years, Don Santiago was honoured as few scientists have ever been. Apart from his nine University Doctorates, coming not only from foreign Universities like Cambridge, Louvain, Wurzburg, Bordeaux, but also Mexico and Guatemala, he was Member or Academician of nearly sixty learned societies, including those in Dublin, Berlin, Coimbra, Buenos Aires and Venezuela. The youth from Petilla de Aragon who had found it hard to pass his school examinations, was member or president of several intellectual groups in Spain itself, and was even designated officially as an 'illustrious and favourite child of the province of Zaragoza'. He was not merely known to his own students at Madrid, but celebrated, and a subscription was got up to provide him with the insignia of his Order of Isabel, and people showered his children with toys. Yet Cajal found that being a great man had a bitter taste. Its first result was to drag him away from his microscope to answer the avalanche of telegrams, letters and cards from all over the world. Then came a solemn occasion when he had to give an oration to the Faculty and students of the University of Madrid. He chose to address them not upon histology, but upon ethics and patriotism, and in doing that, he gave an outline of his own personal creed.

It was a delicate choice for Cajal. His situation now indeed was the very opposite of the old *oposiciones*. He could hardly dwell upon his own merits, yet to deny them altogether would seem inverted arrogance. He presented himself to the students as a man of no more than average endowment, yet possessed with an indomitable will determined to succeed at all costs to itself. And now in their presence, he dedicated himself anew to the service of the University, just as a soldier would make his vows to the Blessed Virgin Mary. He appealed to their patriotism. Spain's glory was departed, her possessions were shrunk, therefore let Spaniards say to themselves all the more firmly — 'To a small country a great soul'. The pen was indeed more mighty than the sword. Let Spain produce so richly that no foreigner would be able to work in any part of the scientific field without meeting Spanish ideas.

In the great hall of the University they heard him with

silence and respect. Ramon y Cajal always gave to his words a message of imperious vitality, and Spaniards could not choose but hear. That University address was his first experiment in mass suggestion.

The phrases he used, when read over in cold blood, appear stale and worn, but their impression was strong. The ideas he placed before his fellow countrymen were not those which had caused such excited approval when delivered in the hall of Clark University, Worcester, Mass. Here in Madrid, there was no praise of materialism, no worship of Germany, no contrast between live America and decadent Europe. Here at home his appeal was spiritual, ethical: the theme was harsh and homely — Spain's discontent and Spain's greatness. He strove to arouse those old qualities of fortitude and adventure, the spirit of the Spanish conquerors who subdued half the world with crucifix and sword.

Upon such an occasion, it would have been unwise to dwell upon that underside of his career of which everyone now praised the brilliant surface. When the tree blossoms, the struggles of the roots are overlooked. After all, he had been unwilling to take up anatomy, had wished to be a painter, had not realized his true direction until he was nearly thirty. The career which everyone now admired had been derived from hatred of discipline, and resistance to his father's purpose. He had not been born with a will to science, his will had created itself. What a strange confession it would have seemed to the professors — and hero-worshipping students. Santiago Ramon was no more responsible for his success than one of the smallest neurones blindly following its imperious way through the developing brain. Yet that is not the way in which prophets are made.

No. Scientific determinism could form no part of that oration. The rebellion of a youth is not the wisdom of a man. Now he was mature, he knew that will power is inspired through imagination. Those hearers in the University heard him spellbound, like primitive men listening to a magician who, in an outburst of candour, has told them that the means of controlling things lies not in ways external to themselves, but in the cultivation of their own faculties.

Alas. He preached, but could not unify, no more than Donna Isabel had been able to do. Spain lived on still in the shadow of her two immense services to Europe — her expulsion of the Moors, and her discovery of America.

Cajal suffered the fate of every prophet. They accepted his achievement, and ignored the ethics. To Spaniards, he was only a professor, a teacher of histology. If he must play at Don Quixote, he would have to lead them not with his visions, but with his microscope.

His advice to scientists became systematized over the years and eventually flowered into a book translated under the title of *Precepts and Counsels of Scientific Investigation*. It is stimulating and full of acid wisdom.

The first beneficial consequence of being officially a great man was that the Government gave Ramon y Cajal a national laboratory such as was taken for granted in Jena and Göttingen. He could surround himself with pupils, could animate those easy-going young Spaniards with a stiffer purpose and they found him no mild taskmaster. Trained in his methods, those youngsters turned out well-prepared sections. The young dog learned to imitate the tricks of the old lion. What he had taught himself with the sweat and tears of two decades, they picked up without tears.

One of these pupils indeed, the gifted Rio del Hortega, would even have the luck to observe one predominant feature of that brain forest which had been quite unnoticed by the head forester — as will be described presently. Though Cajal had now attained what he most desired — a well-equipped institute such as the Germans had — the grapes tasted sour in his mouth. That handsome establishment on the hill named *Instituto Cajal* seemed too pretentious. He was seldom seen in the lofty room appointed to his use, and hung with the original drawings, the 'old masters' of the science of brain histology, but preferred to work in his own house, as he had always done, with the simplest tools. An honoured name abroad was finer than a gilded bench at home.

That first quarterly journal of microscopic science, which he had launched in Barcelona — the *Revista*, now received a rejuvenating injection of official funds. It was rebaptized *Trabajos del Laboratorio de Investigaciones Biologicas*, and later titled in the French language also. The old *Revista* died with the old century, and its more ambitious successor began in 1901. The first number contained six full-scale articles by Cajal, upon particular structures of the brain such as the *olfactory bulb* and the *geniculate* body. The new journal was printed on good paper, and there were lithographs without stint. Don Justo's ambition to publish an anatomy textbook in Zaragoza had been far surpassed.

CHAPTER XXXIII

NEURONE IN DANGER

ATTENDING those great international conferences made the life of a prominent scientist rather like that of a concert virtuoso. Months of private preparation were followed by a public appearance, and the name of Ramon y Cajal on the programme promised an original performance. His friend Van Gehuchten of Louvain University might make a fresh report upon the roots of motor cells in the spinal cord, and Unna, the great skin specialist of Hamburg, describe a new layer of cutaneous cells stained by Cajal's own method. Lantern slides of much magnified sections appeared on the screen above the speaker's head, and outside in the lobby, a row of microscopes invited the members of the conference to investigate for themselves. They were well rewarded. Cajal had admirers in every laboratory. In the evening in some University hall, the leading histologists of the world were seen, a glass of beer in hand, debating some perplexing aspect of the neurone, while their wives vainly attempted to liberate the conversation.

Indeed, the neurone doctrine had come once more into danger, mainly through the revelation of new details in cell architecture. The more the nerve cell was examined, the greater became its complexity. Using a fresh staining technique, one observer had reported an 'enigmatic warp of granular fibrils' actually crossing the body of the cell. What became of these fibrils? And what was their purpose? It was tempting to believe that they were the thread-like precursors of the thick nerve rope that eventually formed the *axon*. One Hungarian histologist (who possessed the disconcerting name of Apáthy) had caused these fibrils to stand out in a clear violet colour, by using a gold stain, but others had failed to repeat his performance. Nothing was to be taken for granted; for working at such high magnifications, the histologist could easily go astray. Cajal, as the leading defender of the neurone became anxious, not through any weakening of belief, but because he felt some points still remained obscure.

The neurone was discussed at an international conference of medicine, held in Madrid in 1903, when Cajal was president of the section of anatomy. The 'network' theory had been placed upon the programme. It might be wondered that Cajal, whose researches had taken the life out of this conception, should have allowed it to be discussed by such an important conference when he himself was chairman. But he did this deliberately. Indeed he had specially invited the leading protagonist of the 'network', Professor Bethe of Strasbourg, to present his views. As president of the section Cajal wished to have this doctrine clearly presented, so that its falsity could be finally rejected. A vigorous tournay between leading histologists was looked for, and Cajal confidently expected the victory.

We may wonder that the issue of a question of science, which is based on pure observation, could be so indefinite as to depend upon public debate at an international conference. Matters of science might be thought to have sharp contours, with no room for individual interpretation. The very reverse is true. All scientific discoveries leave immense scope for reason and intuition, and their devotees are not less human than international statesmen or economists. On this occasion in 1903, there was an anticlimax. The leader of the 'network' forces failed to appear in Madrid. A set of his microscopic slides were sent to Cajal's laboratory carefully packed, and with them, a message from the absent Professor Bethe: 'Treat these slides carefully and return them. They are exceptionally good ones, in fact they are the best we have.' With much anticipation, the preparations were placed under the microscope, and Cajal examined them to find that hypothetical link between the cell-warp and the *axon* fibres which had been so confidently proclaimed from Strasbourg as proof of the 'network' theory. Cajal could find no such connection. The slides were no better than his own. They were duly returned to Strasbourg.

Cajal perceived that the 'network' question could be settled only by a completely fresh staining technique. He still believed firmly in the independence, integrity of the neurone. Yet he hankered after a method, a new method, of proof. Those newly discovered fibrils *inside the cell* were a loud challenge, and he needed a stain that would cause them to stand out clearly against the background of cell contents. Silver, gold, had been tried, but no solution gave convincing results. Somewhere, he was sure in the realm of chemistry, there must be a formula that would attach itself solely to the fibrils. After the Madrid Conference of 1903 which had proved so inconclusive, his mind was obsessed with this problem. Whether he was sitting at the laboratory bench, or walking home from the *Café Suizo* through the *Retiro* gardens, fibrils and stains, silver and gold, neurones and *axons* were always in his thoughts.

A journey to Italy—that was surely a way to calm such persistent ruminations! With Señora Cajal, and his sisters, he set out upon holiday. They visited Milan, and Rome, and as far south as Naples. But a creative mind cannot leave its problems at home. His recent strains, the Conference, the fatigue of setting up the *Instituto Cajal*, bringing out the second issue of the *Trabajos* which contained seven original papers by its editor—were certainly lessened as he wandered in the Pitti Gallery, taking photographs of churches and palaces. But he could never keep away from laboratories, and when he reached the hotel questions of staining returned. Every step in his method was re-examined. One solution was too alkaline, perhaps: another mixture had been too weak. The ladies found him absent-minded as they walked round the Academy at Venice. He was dreaming of stains rather than of Tintorettos and Titians. His own masterpiece was still unproduced, and his technique pursued him relentlessly. Gradually out of this artist's concentration, one substance emerged; it was silver, the metal through which he had made his name. In Golgi's stain, the silver was capable of attaching itself to the *axon* fibres, but how was it to be made to stain those elusive neurofibrils, the strands *inside* the nerve cell? As he used his camera in Florence and Venice, Cajal could not think of a means of forcing the silver to cling just where he wished it to be.

Then, came the creative moment. Often, the flash called inspiration occurs merely by a variation of the familiar. Until that decisive second, he had thought of every detail, except the one that was now obvious the moment he had seen it. Why not use silver nitrate *hot*?

From this point the Italian holiday became a failure.

Along the Riviera coast of Italy and France, the autumn flowers and the sea made no impression. Ramon y Cajal was in a dream. Repeating to himself that *heated* silver nitrate must surely attach itself to the neurofibrils, he was miserable because he could not be at his laboratory bench. Perhaps, after all, it was only a will-o'-the-wisp — as Golgi's method had proved so often before. Home again in Madrid, he threw himself upon some nerve sections like a lion upon its prey.

It was not so easy, or so quick, to devour this morsel. A block of tissue must be placed in a bath of silver nitrate and heated for four days. Haste would ruin everything. His patience was strained even further while the tissue was developed in Pyrogallic acid. Then, he must control his hands while cutting the sections. Ramon y Cajal was never calm in such moments, yet calm he must be. He looked at his preparation stained in the new way.

Before his eyes was a revelation. Never had he observed any stained tissue that was so beautifully displayed with all the details of its architecture. And prominent there were those mysterious neurofibrils — they were indeed woven through the body of the cell, like the strands in a peasant-made basket. Each fibril was so perfectly invested with metallic silver, that it showed up russet or black against a burnt-brown background. These parasitic chloride and bromide deposits (found in previous techniques, and the bane of the histologist) were entirely absent. Heated silver nitrate was indeed an extra sense, a new tool. There was now no doubt as to the meaning of those inner fibrils. He could see them clearly, originating in the dendrites (those horns that stick out of the cell like antlers) then, after twining across and around the cell body in rich profusion, they gathered in a bunch and passed down the *axons*, thus providing proof of that continuous conducting mechanism which Cajal's theory of 'dynamic polarization' required. Wherever in the nervous system such neurofibrils existed, the new stain would infallibly reveal them, dark or golden brown.

The greatest discoveries are made sometimes by those most indebted to their forerunners.

During those same early years of the present century when Cajal was making his theory out of precise observations, another scientist, Guglielmo Marconi, was working in the opposite direction — converting an abstract theory into practical form. In a shed on the coast of Cornwall, he was handling etheric waves, first discovered by Heinrich Hertz, passing them through a valve invented by Ambrose Fleming, for transmission across the Atlantic. Radio was born out of that successful adaptation of a theory.

Many physicists had read the scientific papers of Heinrich Hertz, just as all histologists were familiar with the silver nitrate of Camillo Golgi. Only Marconi had the genius to make those rays cross to Newfoundland; only Cajal had caused the heated silver solution to reveal the neurofibrils.

CHAPTER XXXIV

NOBEL TWINS

THE passage of Cajal's life had almost ceased to be chronicled in years. In place of 1904 and 1905 were issues of the *Trabajos del Laboratorio de Investigaciones Biologicas*, volumes three and four, filled largely with papers by its founder and editor. Cajal had indeed come to live fully the pages of his journal. Its photogravures were now more numerous and more elaborate, and his contributions dealt with more unfamiliar subjects in the nervous system which acquired importance from the prominence he gave them. His labour in that narrow field had surpassed that of anyone else. Silently in those ten years since his visit to London, his reputation became world wide. At the age of fifty-four his full stature was declared.

Early one October morning in 1906, before daylight had crossed the Guadarrama, a *telegrama* was delivered. Its wording was unusually terse and economical. It contained only five words in German, as though the sender knew that so pregnant a message needed nothing more. The telegram came from Sweden, and the signature was of Emil Holmgren, a professor in the Medical Faculty of Stockholm. Only that familiar name reassured Ramon y Cajal that he was not a victim of hallucination. The message read — CAROLINE INSTITUTE AWARDS YOU NOBEL PRIZE. That was all. Well had the Professor calculated that such an announcement required no comment.

To receive one of Alfred Nobel's awards was the rarest

intellectual distinction, and only once before had it
come to Spain, when in 1904 José Echegaray had been
honoured for his dramatic writing. Earlier in his life,
being a Spaniard had been a disadvantage for Cajal.
Now, the rarity of the prize fitted the uniqueness of his
status. Fortune is a woman, and never shows moderation
either in her indifference, or her largesse. A year
before this, Cajal had been awarded the even rarer
Helmholtz Medal by the Royal Academy of Sciences of
Berlin. The Medal itself weighed 620 grammes of gold
and was accompanied by a replica in copper. Even
heavier was the avalanche of congratulations which held
up his work for weeks. Now, the Nobel Prize caused a
new explosion. When he heard details that were
conveyed in that laconic telegram, Cajal's embarrassment became displeasure.

He found that he had been awarded the Nobel Prize
not as a pure scientist, but in the section of 'Physiology
and Medicine'. This gave him a feeling of irregularity, of
distaste. It was the nineteenth-century idea that
medicine is less honourable than science. There was an
echo too of Don Justo's scorn of the pure physician with
his gold cane and scarlet mantle. His work had been
scientific, and he would have been more satisfied to have
it recognized as such. But the authorities of the Caroline
Institute in Stockholm had followed the same policy in
previous years. They had given a wide interpretation to
the term 'physiology and medicine'. In 1902 their
choice in this department had been Emil von Behring
whose discovery of diphtheria antitoxin was certainly
based upon a laboratory technique just as precise as that
of Cajal. The next Nobel prize-winner in the same
section was Sir Ronald Ross. Certainly his work upon

the transmission of malaria through the mosquito was a triumph for the scientific method. Then in 1905 there was Robert Koch, who found the cause of tuberculosis, an achievement as great in theory as it became in practice. Ivan Pavlov, the Russian physiologist who described reflex action had also been Cajal's predecessor in this honourable line. The judges in Stockholm had been perfectly consistent in placing him in the same category as these men. It was no small distinction to be measured with von Behring, Ross, Koch and Pavlov. Though histology is a branch of physiology, it is pursued for the value it brings to medicine.

Cajal's irritation can be traced to another cause. When he saw the complete list of prize-winners, he was horrified to find his own name bracketed with that of Camillo Golgi, Professor in Pavia and *Senatore* of the Kingdom of Italy, who had invented, then neglected, the silver bichromate stain. With complete impartiality, though some failure of later information, the Swedes had joined them together, as though they represented the same views. Oil and water could not be more different.

Ramon y Cajal had used the silver stain with practically every tissue of the nervous system, and had published his results in a hundred scientific papers, each one giving credit to Golgi's name. In its author's own hands, silver bichromate had been an uncertain performer, and Golgi had lost interest. Only Cajal's persistence had brought out its real value. It was the later developments — as for instance Cajal's using the solution heated — which had given the method its great success, especially in throwing up the hidden neurofibrils. Moreover, it was not the stain alone which was the reason for Cajal's pre-eminence. Its use in the embryo, and in lower animals had enabled him to compare neurones, and introduce the law of 'dynamic polarization'. His final grievance was the fact that Camillo Golgi was still an unrepentant believer in the 'network' theory — although it was virtually abandoned by other histologists.

Their personal relations, even apart from scientific divergence, had never been close. Ramon y Cajal needed cynicism to contemplate a visit to Stockholm in company with *Senatore* Golgi. It is likely that the Swedish judges felt that they could not honour Cajal for work that was based partly on another man's method. Perhaps too those Northerners found it appropriate to make two Latins into a pair. On the only previous occasion when the Nobel Prize came to Spain, José Echegaray had been bracketed with the French Provençal poet Frederic Mistral.

Sympathy can be felt for him during those last few weeks of 1906 while he was preparing for the journey to Stockholm in time for December 10th, Alfred Nobel's birthday. He must pack his bag and look cheerful. Meanwhile he must embrace, as tolerantly as possible, fame's ugly sister, publicity. Newspapers in Madrid which had ignored the Professor now turned the Nobel Prize into a commodity called News. Streets were named *Calle Ramon y Cajal* in small Spanish towns. Schoolboys wrote to him for his autograph. Chocolate and lemonade were called after him. Financiers wrote that he had only to permit them to make use of his reputation — nothing more — and substantial profits would accrue to himself! He was obliged to give up his laboratory and spend the whole day answering that idiot mass of congratulations. In the evenings, he must attend banquets until his digestion revolted. To survive such tributes, would require a heart of steel, the skin of an elephant, and the stomach of a vulture. Latins are extremists. Poverty had been bad enough, but the flatteries with which his fellow countrymen revealed their desire to honour him had become wearisome. The only satisfying notes in this chorus of adulation were the medal subscribed for by the students of San Carlos, the album of tributes from doctors in Valencia, and the testimonial from Spanish-speaking physicians in Buenos Aires. Such well-wishers were at least able to comprehend a neurone, and perhaps even share his disquiet over the linkage with Camillo Golgi. It was some consolation to Cajal that his half share of the Nobel Prize represented a considerable bonus to a professor's income.

Across Europe in winter he took the Northern Express to the capital of Sweden. It was to be more congenial for Cajal to shake hands with the King than with the histologist from Pavia.

The late Alfred Nobel had been a dreamer, a poet, and a most successful man of business. His fortune had come from a simple discovery, made in the 1840s, that cotton wool dissolved in acid, produced a powerful explosive called gun-cotton. From this arose an even more devastating substance called dynamite. Alfred Nobel blasted his way to success, for his products were useful not only in warfare, but in quarrying and mining. The power and danger of this commodity seemed to darken his personal life. He remained an unsatisfied bachelor, deeply attached to his mother. He moved to and fro across Europe, unable to settle anywhere, alternating between solitude and sociability, working in his laboratory, then writing poetry. He admired Shelley and hated organized religion. He believed that science would enable mankind to find happiness and emerge from the dark past. Alfred Nobel died suddenly in 1896, and his will was a surprise to the world.

Like many other clear-headed men who disbelieve in lawyers, Nobel had left his intentions in confusion. A special Act of the Swedish Parliament was required to set up a great fund out of which prizes were to be awarded in different departments of human knowledge, and open to men and women, Swedes and foreigners alike. The bachelor who always believed in medical research had made an earlier bequest for this purpose when his mother died. Now among the awards made by the Carolinska Institute of Stockholm was that for 'Physiology and Medicine'.

In the great hall of the Academy of Music, the bust of Alfred Nobel looking down from a background of flowers, the King of Sweden, Ministers of State, professors and officers faced that handful of world celebrities who had come like schoolboys to receive their prizes. Ramon y Cajal found himself in unexpected company. Alfred Nobel's internationalism had brought together some strange bedfellows. Such incongruous individuals could hardly be expected to produce complete intellectual concord, and the royal personages may have perceived currents of disharmony in that distinguished gathering. Apart from Camillo Golgi, who with his impressive mien and Victor Emmanuel moustache looked every inch a *Senatore*, there was Joseph John Thomson the physicist from Cambridge who had carried on the work of von Röntgen (himself the first Nobel Prize winner) on X-rays. Cajal, also a doctor of Cambridge University, might have preferred to be linked with such a pure scientist as Thomson. There was another of very different distinction, the Italian Giosuè Carducci, now an old man, who forty years before, had been the poet of revolt, and had shocked his country by a hymn to Satan. Cajal's cosmopolitan tolerance was severely tested by the fact that the Nobel Laureate for Peace was President Theodore Roosevelt who, though not in office during the Spanish-American War, represented those American influences that had ousted Spain from her last colony in the New World.

Each Laureate is required to give a brief address describing in general terms befitting an audience not composed of specialists, the work which had brought him this honour. By convention they refer modestly to their own achievements. When his turn came, Camillo Golgi launched upon a paean of self-praise. He went back to his earliest paper, published in an obscure Italian journal, and traced to it a long pedigree of discoveries made by Golgi alone. No mention of other histologists, not even Italians. In that firmament, Golgi was the lone star. The King and notabilities in the Academy of Music were told that all this solitary work performed by the Professor of Pavia had proved that nerve fibres were all woven together in one continuous network. It was as though the speaker had been asleep for years, and had awakened with a start. At the Nobel banquet Golgi repeated his self-sufficient performance.

Ramon y Cajal, when he recovered from his astonishment, could only make a short speech in French, referring to those names whom his Italian colleague had so ostentatiously ignored. On arriving in Stockholm, he had attempted personal relations with Golgi, even going to the railway station to meet him, but their encounter had been unsatisfactory. He felt it was more dignified to leave the matter to the judgment of experts. Between the Italian and the Spanish genius there was the shadow of an ancient rivalry — the old scorn of the nimble inheritor of Rome for the slow proud Iberian. Perhaps Camillo Golgi was inwardly conscious of his failing prestige, and chose this unique moment, as joint prize-winner, to strike his blow.

Once those embarrassing occasions were past the absurd incongruity of the affair must have appealed to Cajal's sense of humour. Over the integrity of the neurone he could never feel half-hearted. Yet the unexpectedness of life, the strange inconsistency between theory and experience — must have tempered his annoyance with cynical amusement.

Stockholm in winter — it was so different from other capitals and so unlike the cities of Spain — islands, dark channels, palaces surrounded by black forests covered with snow, were balm for his feelings. Cajal was at home near mountains. Those short Northern days with early twilight and late sunrise, were a sharp contrast to bare Castile with the half-empty Manzanares throwing around Madrid its boundary of half-dry stones. The cool speech and objective attitude of these Northern people were a change from Latin exuberance. He felt, as he had felt in London, a little envious of their easy ways and serene detachment, which inspired him to make an epigram: 'grey matter grows well under grey skies'. He visited laboratories, and the ancient University of Upsala — no experience to Cajal was ever without interest. And the hosts were delighted with his eager, naive questions; they admired, as perceptive strangers always did, that blending of charm with scientific devotion. As usual when he had enjoyed himself most, Ramon y Cajal was happiest when back home in Madrid. Medical students at Zaragoza saluted his success by subscribing for a gold medal which was struck in his honour.

A prize-winner home from the capital of Sweden, had to justify in his own eyes in the capital of Spain his great reputation in the eyes of others. He would now have to revise his Nobel address for publication in the *Archivio di Fisiologia*; and there was a speech to the Royal Academy of Medicine to be given in June 1907. Studies had to be continued in an original field — that of the degeneration of nerves when severed by accident or disease.

Spain was in one more political crisis; Cajal learned that another of the responsibilities of a Nobel prize-winner was to help to solve it. The new Prime Minister, Don Segismundo Moret, a Liberal and half English by birth, had once many years before during the reign of King Amadeo, been Spanish Ambassador at St. James'. He was a friend of Ramon y Cajal, and now whispered in his ear the agreeable news that he intended to open his political programme with a reform of Spanish education. Would the Professor kindly advise him where to begin? Ramon y Cajal needed no pressure to enlarge upon so congenial a subject. He would certainly give the Minister his opinions.

Eagerly, he gave his diagnosis of Spanish failings, and expounded his remedy to cure them. Education undoubtedly, that was where the cure should begin. Colleges upon the English system — they would be essential. Facilities for games such as he had seen at Harvard, Cambridge, and Cambridge, England, well-equipped laboratories upon the German plan — yes, and naturally, post-graduate opportunities abroad. Cajal talked, with the complete conviction of one who has thought out ideas over many years and hardly dares to hope for their realization. Don Segismundo gave perfect attention. The Professor searched his face for signs of dismay at the inevitable and crushing expense of such a programme. No such signs appeared. The Prime Minister's face remained perfectly calm, even acquiescent. In his innocence of a politician's guile, Cajal had not expected what was to follow. The Prime Minister broke out into enthusiastic agreement. 'Your ideas for the reform of Spanish schooling are the same as my own. You shall be my Minister of Education,' said Segismundo Moret.

Ramon y Cajal was completely nonplussed. To be a minister? He demurred; he was a scientist, not a politician, but Don Segismundo used to managing men had an argument ready. Remember Berthelot — the great Berthelot in France — he was a pure mathematician, and in the Chamber of Deputies he was a great success. Don Segismundo would not let him say No.

Cajal went home, quite bemused at the sudden reversal of the situation — his having intended to convert the Prime Minister to his views, and being in turn himself converted to something different. He applied his histologist's mind to the notion of this glorious chance of achieving for Spain what was dear to his heart. To make his small country worthy of her great soul, and to do this through her colleges and schools, that was an ambition worthy to crown a lifetime. Cajal took his problem in his head while attending a medical congress in Lisbon. He thought over Don Segismundo's plea while questions of histology were being discussed and gradually, among men and ideas where he was at home, the humiliations of a politician's career became more obvious; his friends in laboratories would shake their heads over poor Cajal who had deserted science, while those clever *politicos* would have no respect for a mere biologist. After all, the Liberal party of Don Segismundo Moret was only one party, and not particularly strong. Ambition urged him to accept. Intuition told him to stick to the microscopic world where he was supreme and renounce the *Cortes* where he would be an unpractised innocent. He returned to Madrid, and wrote to the Prime Minister begging to be excused.

Don Segismundo overwhelmed him with reproaches; he had hoped to exploit the prestige of a Nobel prizewinner; like all politicians he was thinking more of the man who suited his purpose than the programme which was, perhaps, no more than a programme. Another professor was chosen to be Minister of Education.

Ramon y Cajal missed his chance to reform education, though it came to him a second time in the form of the *Junta para Ampliacion de los Estudios* which was formed in 1907. He had shown himself a shrewd prophet, for Don Segismundo's ministry did not last long. Cajal's Quixotic qualities had been overborne by that caution that distinguishes Spaniards of the north-east. Says Miguel de Unamuno, 'Only he who attempts the absurd is capable of achieving the impossible'.

Cajal's educational influence was confined to the *junta*, and to his new Institute on the hill where a younger generation of histologists learned to make sections, under those eyes whose concentration had founded this world-famous school of histology.

CHAPTER XXXV

THE MASTER AND HIS PUPILS

IN the unpretentious room, with homely and home-made apparatus, the Nobel prizewinner worked at his own little patch of biology. As he looked down the microscope upon that Lilliputian world in which colour meant so much, the entire universe of the tissues had become his province. Half a century of exploring those cells, nuclei, and fibres had given him unique authority. Cajal was an inspiring teacher, but not an easy master, and one given to sudden explosions of wrath. A student who threw some orange peel during his lecture heard the Professor challenge him there and then to go outside the lecture room and settle this affair with their fists. Presumably that student was not aware of the athlete of Zaragoza. Mostly however, the Professor was calm, absorbed in his work.

The fruits of Golgi's stain were rich. In twenty years since Cajal had revealed its potentialities, twenty modifications had come into use, and even Golgi had become interested once more. A German physician, Bielschowsky had applied it to tumours, cerebral haemorrhage, and other diseased conditions of the brain. Silver bichromate had led many travellers into the brain forest.

They sent their papers to the journals, and others could test whether the adaptation gave reliable results. Camillo Golgi himself, nettled by Cajal's success had modified his first idea by using an arsenic solution to follow the silver, and this, Cajal considered an improvement; it rendered those nerve strands more prominent as they crossed the cell and passed into the *axon*. Golgi introduced a further improvement — uranium salts to give even more intensification. The quest for clarity was unending. Truth in histology seemed to depend upon luck in choosing an appropriate chemical. Yet some observers did not have the lucky touch. They found it easy to lose their way, and misinterpreted what they saw. Once again, the neurone doctrine was seriously challenged. From different laboratories came a breath of the old heresy — that nerve fibres can arise independently of nerve cells, and Cajal's friend van Gehuchten of the University of Louvain was seemingly converted. This was hard for Cajal who loved the Flemish professor as a man and a scientist and with his usual thoroughness, he took out his familiar material, his sections made from many tissues, and marshalled once again the evidence, from mammals, worms, crustaceans.

Everything strengthened his belief that the neurone was independent, that the neurofibrils never arose from anywhere but the nerve cell, and that those delicate endings of the *axon*, however intimately they might appear to touch other cells, never genuinely made contact. A fresh illustration of the meaning of neurone integrity had come to hand. There was now evidence, that in sleep, or after narcotic drugs, the terminal fibrils of one cell actually drew apart from those of the next, so that no electrical current could pass between them since communication from one cell to another was interrupted. Charles Sherrington had named this gateway through which the nerve impulse passed from one neurone to the next, a *synapse*. Such *synapses* it appeared, could be open or shut. Would this do for an explanation of the mechanism of sleep? Was sleep then no more than a general retarding of nervous activity, due to the millions of tiny obstacles set up by this diminished ease of transmission?

It was an attractive theory, and though hard to prove, it gave an even greater coherence to Cajal's belief in neurone individuality. If the nerve fibre could thus withdraw from active participation in nervous activity — if when a majority of cells did so, sleep was the result, did that not support his general theory that the brain has evolved out of independent competing units? Those neurones, however much they might resemble electric batteries, were alive, they had a skill such as no contrivance of copper and zinc could ever have — the power to draw back their tentacles and isolate themselves from fellow neurones. It was a startling illumination. However mechanical the nervous system might appear when seen in wax sections, however much one might call in electrical ideas to explain it, there was clearly some vitalism working in the background. These neurones were endowed with life, and a power of independence.

Yet the 'network' theory was still raising its head. Friends urged Ramon y Cajal as leader of the neurone school to defend his doctrine. Though naturally tenacious, he disliked controversy, unlike some professors, and it grieved him to contradict his friend from Louvain. In a long series of papers over more than twenty-five years, he maintained his faith. Between 1906, that wonderful year of the Helmholtz Medal and Nobel Prize, and 1914, when his research took a new turn, Cajal produced over fifty papers upon an almost unbelievable variety of aspects of the neurone. He continued defending the doctrine till the end of his life, almost his final scientific paper being 'Neuronismo o Reticularismo?' His defence even came from beyond the grave, in a chapter entitled *Die Neuronlehre* which appeared in a German textbook, after his death.

Among those who worked in the *Instituto Cajal* was a gifted graduate from Valladolid, Pio del Rio Hortega, who had become an expert histologist. His regard for Ramon y Cajal was reverential. It was this pupil's fate to commit an act of penetration that was almost an imprudence. Using a modification of the original metallic stain, Rio Hortega observed a type of cell that did not fit into any established category. It possessed only a short *axon*. Such cells were numerous and ubiquitous, and seemed to form a background to the more familiar elements of the nervous system. He showed them to the *Señor Profesor*, at first with some hesitation.

It was not to be expected that a man who had been examining nerve tissues for forty years would be ready to welcome this important discovery made in his own Institute but which had escaped him entirely. Ramon y Cajal accepted what his pupil now showed him. It was agreed that the new cells were vitally important. In fact, they form a soft mass of supporting tissue, which surrounds the more active elements of the brain, and constitutes a jelly-like matrix in which they function. The new tissue was named *mesoglia*, though the more usual term is now *microglia*. It was in fact a discovery of fundamental importance. *Microglia* might be compared to the *humus* of the soil, into which trees send down their roots. Yet *microglia* is a living, an active tissue, which envelops the conducting nerve cells. Charles Sherrington called it by a curious name — a 'benign parasite'.

Pio del Rio Hortega had indeed made a magnificent discovery, for which Cajal gave him full credit.

Yet something in the personality of his gifted pupil produced irritation in the master's soul. His own failure to observe the *microglia* was like missing the wood for the trees. His lapse had been big. Outwardly Cajal was proud that this success had come to his own laboratory, and not to Berlin or Göttingen, yet he was human, and he was the son of that fiercely possessive Justo Ramon. Even in the austere atmosphere of science, fatalities of human discord occur between world fame and aspiring youth. Some tale-bearing attendant played the part of messenger in this Greek drama of the laboratory. A chance remark which del Rio Hortega had dropped was twisted and repeated to the Professor, and there was an Olympian explosion of thunder. Not waiting for apology or explanation, Ramon y Cajal fell upon the discoverer of the *microglia* with a torrent of reproaches, and del Rio Hortega who was not made of Aragon rock but of more sensitive material, dissolved in tears. The affront to his nature was so deep that he left the laboratory, and never again worked with Cajal. The man who found the *microglia* was sure of a welcome elsewhere. Pio del Rio Hortega worked in Oxford, and later became Professor in Buenos Aires. He always acknowledged the greatness of his teacher and later they became reconciled.

From that human episode we see the Professor was not an easy man to work with. Don Justo Ramon had left his impression upon Santiago; the son of a dominant parent had grown to be a dominating master towards his intellectual sons.

They were now scattered throughout the world especially so in South America where a group of Cajal's admirers published in two volumes, a complete edition of his papers, with a eulogistic introduction. The master in Madrid was delighted. His fervour of gratitude showed typical Hispanic exaggeration. Everything in Argentina was perfect, just as everything in Spain was the reverse, since all the best Spaniards had gone to South America. His pride permitted him to talk thus only to fellow speakers of Spanish, who alone would understand the patriotism that allowed him to criticize his own country.

CHAPTER XXXVI

VISION AND ITS CHALLENGE

DURING the first World War, Spain was neutral and as often before and since in European history, the Iberian peninsula became virtually an island. Such isolation was to most Spaniards more congenial than to Cajal, for Spaniards are apt to despise Europe. To him, an internationalist and scientific visionary, this war was a bitter frustration. Countries where he had so many friends were now bitter enemies. He missed those visitors from Wurzburg, Jena, Berlin. European culture and tradition seemed to be drifting towards suicide. At one time, he had been ashamed of the intellectual backwardness of Spain. Now, it was the other way round. With Switzerland, his own country was almost alone in her devotion to the sciences of peace.

Cajal had always been an admirer of Germany. Her Universities were well organized, her industries so soundly based upon her Universities. Now, it was a paradox, those successful industries had been diverted from commerce to war. Here was a great country, of indisputable influence and culture, which had gone mad. It was insane enough to make war upon its own admirers, its disciples and customers, a war that could end only in poverty and misery. Yet Germany had chosen this moment to present him with her highest distinction, the Prussian Order 'Pour le Mérite', to which Frederick the Great had once appointed Voltaire.

His own materialistic outlook, so typical of the nineteenth century now wavered, as his enthusiasm for German culture declined. Cajal's friend Van Gehuchten had been driven out of Louvain University when the German armies advanced, and had taken refuge in England from where he wrote despairing letters to Madrid. They had known one another over a quarter of a century, and though the Flemish professor had wavered over the neurone theory, Cajal felt that he understood the genius of Spain, as was natural in a Fleming whose country had once been governed by Charles V. Then Van Gehuchten died in exile. Final disillusionment over Germany was to come only in the last years of Cajal's life, which corresponded with the rise of Adolf Hitler.

Though growing more critical of Germany, Cajal was not any more tolerant of his own country. Spaniards he was convinced, had latent genius, quite equal to that of the French or the Germans; yet Spanish neurones undoubtedly needed stimulus. It was as though the dread inhibitions of the Dominican Prior of Salamanca, Tomas Torquemada, had never ceased circulating in the Spanish soul since the Inquisition which he had conducted with such ghastly efficiency. In his *Instituto Cajal* the Professor laboured to neutralize the dark legacy of that fifteenth-century intoxication. Cajal was now in his sixties, and in the weariness of his disappointment with Europe, he concentrated all his energies upon Spain, like a lone Quixote pursuing his ideal.

There were family troubles too. His eldest son who seemed to have inherited his own gifts, suffered from heart disease, and there could be no question of any strenuous training. This boy's life had no orchard-robbing, no *Telemache* in a mountain cave, though we cannot imagine that Don Justo's son was an easy father. Don Santiago hoped to make him a medical bookseller, so that one day they would publish together the book he was writing on Scientific Photography — just as in the old days at Zaragoza, Don Justo and Santiago had dreamed of an illustrated textbook of anatomy. In those forty intervening years, the process of lithography had advanced considerably, and Ramon y Cajal had mastered the art of reproduction. But the second hope was to be as barren as the first. His eldest boy died, and the father had to bring out his book alone.

Photography was some relief in his tribulations. It belonged to that part of his mind where instinct had given him a fascination for the world as seen through vision. The photographic plate covered with silver salts was it not merely an imitation of the human eye? The staining of neurofibrils, it was just a trick, copied from photography!

Cajal's own visual gift — so rich, so exact and persistent, deserves to be compared with that of the greatest of Spanish painters, Diego Silva y Velazquez, born two and a half centuries before.

Velazquez was the most faithful recorder of objective experience that art has ever known. Upon his canvas, he registered the sensations of the eye, using brushes with the accuracy of a photograph, yet perceiving more than any camera. His sombre portraits of Philip IV, with Hapsburg chin and blonde Hapsburg hair, his pictures, equally serious, of those terrible dwarfs, the misshapen playthings of the Court — have the same impartial fidelity. Velazquez never comments, never explains. He has no philosophy like Rembrandt, no mysticism like El Greco. It might be said that Velazquez possesses the clear and cool judgment of a scientist, allied with supreme art.

In the same spirit, Ramon y Cajal approached the subject matter of histology. Religious intensity, and mysticism — so characteristic of Spain, was absent from Cajal, just as from Velazquez. Both men were brilliant recorders, because they had developed, in their vastly differing ways, the visual art to perfection. A glance through Cajal's textbook of histology shows hundreds of reproductions, faithful records of cells, fibres, nuclei — all the phenomena of the microscopic tissues. Yet they are not mere transcriptions. These pictures are a thousand times more clear than any photograph which can render only the plethora and profusion of nature. The same artistic freshness, combined with scientific exactitude, is found in those botanical illustrators like Jan van Huysum, who can represent a flower, a leaf, an insect settling upon a decayed apple, with a clearness that makes the best photograph seem crude. Later, Cajal's gift of conveying truth in illustrations will be compared to that of the artist J. J. Audubon.

It was thus no accident that the theme which most fascinated Cajal, to the end of his life, was the study of the complex mechanism of seeing. In his bitterness over the Spanish defeat of 1898, he had found consolation there, and had refuted the great Kölliker. Now again, he found relief from his sadness over the European war, in this same theme. To repel sadness, the mother of inaction, he forced himself back to life which was energy, renovation, and progress. The result of his second exploration of the visual theme turned out vastly different from the first. It was to be like one of those adventures into a new world forest that bewitch the traveller and send him home doubting the reality of his own experience.

What Cajal had successfully disputed with von Kölliker nearly twenty years before — the phenomenon of binocular vision — was now accepted. Cajal had become familiar with other intriguing facts about vision in lower animals, and there were further points he wished to clear up. With his life's experience, his technique, his will power, he had no doubts that he would soon achieve this completeness. He began with insects, believing that the insect eye would be found comparatively simple.

It was his sense of system which made him begin, so to speak, at the bottom, among those humble insects. Once they had revealed to him their uncomplicated secrets, he would work upwards through the crustacea, fishes, amphibians — towards man. Cajal was nearly seventy when he set out upon this research, for which all his life's experience had prepared him. Never was any quest to prove so unrewarding. Those lowly insects whose eyes he expected to find so simple, have a power of vision so stupendous as to make the eye of man simple in comparison.

When he came to compare different animal eyes Cajal found them as diverse as the headgear of Spanish peasants which, for no obvious reason differ from valley to valley. Some animals indeed possess more than one kind of visual organ which are used for different purposes.

What delighted yet perplexed him most was the eye of the insect. Its intricacy beggared description. As he examined his slides taken from the moth or the bumble bee, Cajal felt humbled. There was also that wonderful 'compound' eye of the dragon fly, made up of a hundred facets — really a whole battery of eyes. In comparison with the moth's eye, that of Velazquez was elementary. For the moth's receiving disc was not single but triple, and the connection between right and left was not one bridge, as in man, but three bridges. Each separate stage in the relay system between insect eye and insect brain was reduplicated beyond the power of the microscope to observe or the mind to conceive.

Ramon y Cajal reached the humiliating conclusion that the more he studied vision in those humble creatures without backbones, the less he understood the marvellous nature of its organization. He had always been a convinced Darwinian, and had assumed that nature moved 'upwards' — from a 'lower' towards the 'higher' form of life. He was finding this assumption to be unsound. In designing the visual apparatus, nature had not taken a straight path, but advanced by twists, and sometimes even went backwards.

An instance of this was the so-called 'panoramic vision' found in reptiles — a useful device for co-ordinating what is seen with the pair of eyes. But mammals had thrown aside panoramic vision altogether, and had gone back to the system of using each eye separately, a method which had compelled the introduction of the 'crossing' of nerve fibres. What purpose could there be in such retrogression? Nature, it seemed, was not only the mother of invention. She was the mother of waste. Out of her boundless resourcefulness, she discovered practical devices. Then she threw them away with prodigal indifference.

Perhaps Cajal's previous view of evolution had been over-simplified and even Charles Darwin might not have agreed with it. Certainly, these researches into the eye had contradicted any assumption of regular progress — from the simple to the more complex.

Vision had become an obsession with Cajal. It was reflected in the papers he published during those years. In 1915, he had described the 'fundamental plan of the retina of insects'. In 1917, 'the retina and optic centres in cephalopods'. During the next year, the *Trabajos* (now in its sixteenth volume) contained a communication, illustrated with twenty-four plates, upon 'the structure of the eyes and optic nerves in certain insects'. The series went on during 1921, 1922, until 1923, when Cajal's observations upon cats, ants and rodents were published. After this, his concentration upon vision came to an end. From a philosophical point of view, it had ended in defeat.

He had begun with the naive assumption that insects were 'lowly' forms of life. He had found the opposite. As he peered through his microscope at these Lilliputian forms, the thought came to him (as it had come to Jean Henri Fabre) that nature had bestowed her crowning mental gift not upon man, but upon the bees, the moths, and the ants. She had endowed them with a mind possessing the power of instant and decisive action, a mind which had achieved its perfection millions of years before it was ousted from its throne by the coarse brains of fish, amphibian and man. It was indeed a sombre conclusion for a nineteenth-century child of Charles Darwin. His research into the histology of the visual apparatus, begun with such optimistic anticipations, had brought Cajal to a point where he was obliged to question his scientific faith. This Spanish Socrates, accustomed to putting questions to nature and having those questions answered, had reached such a perverse and paradoxical conclusion that he felt a chill of depression, as though his life's work had become void.

In 1922, his seventieth year, Ramon y Cajal handed over the Institute to the control of his friend and pupil Don Francisco Tello, but continued himself to work in that home laboratory which he preferred. A complimentary work in two large volumes, containing tributes by his friends and pupils was presented to him as a parting gift at this close of his purely professional life.

In future, his personal labours in histology were likely to give diminishing returns. His great contemporary Sigmund Freud, who was still probing the nervous system, though from a very different standpoint, had reached similar doubt. Towards the end of his life, Freud had a glimpse of the vast areas of truth that stretched beyond the limits of what he had so patiently revealed. There is one further interesting analogy between Cajal and the founder of Psychoanalysis.

Reading Freud's book on Dreams, Cajal had noted how futile the idea of sleep as the great consoler had become since Freud had shown man's nocturnal repose to be a theatre of violent and disconcerting activity. As he thought over his own researches into vision, Cajal felt the same shock of surprise. The eye of the dragon fly held more truth than any theorem of science or philosophy. His own special gift, his seeing yet innocent eye, had suddenly proved unable to see any more.

He remembered, as a schoolboy in Huesca, the wrath of Don Vicente Ventura, that zealot who preached so firmly against Freethinkers, Liberals, sceptics, and foretold their eventual defeat and confusion. Now, at the close of his purely scientific career Ramon y Cajal understood that intellectual dilemma which awaits the scientist who has observed more details than he is able to explain. This scientists' nihilism — was it the final bourne of the sceptic, as the vehement Don Vicente had foretold?

CHAPTER XXXVII

CAJAL THE PHILOSOPHER

IN the great park of the city of Madrid, the *Buen Retiro*, along well swept paths between chestnut trees arranged in squares and quincunxes like an Arabian garden, the Professor took his favourite walk, to the café and homeward. His thoughts were probably dwelling on the forthcoming issue of the *Trabajos*, though not exclusively, for this learned man was no hermit. He pondered, he dreamed, but that did not prevent the enjoyable use of his senses. His eyes still looked brilliant, still saw much. Nursemaids wheeled their babies, and gardeners in velveteens, picturesquely armed with a carbine and a horn, saluted Don Santiago, and ladies strolling in the *Buen Retiro* found his approving glances resting upon them. His physical vitality made the world smile admiringly, and it was whispered that he must have paid a visit to the Paris specialist Voronoff whose experiments upon rejuvenation had become notorious before their limitations were understood. The subject was much in the air during the nineteen-twenties and is referred to in Cajal's last book. We have no further evidence on the subject, but Don Santiago was the sort of man about whom such things were likely to be mentioned. Certainly his aphorisms about the female sex, his masculine and tolerant point of view, do not give the impression of being based upon theory.

After years of enjoyment of his walk through the gardens, he was obliged to change his regular circuit among those familiar paths. The authorities had erected in the *Buen Retiro* a group of symbolic statuary overlooking a fountain and pool, and Ramon y Cajal felt embarrassment on passing that way. The marble figure gazing into the depth of the water, as though searching for hidden truths — represented himself. It was a memorial to the great Spanish histologist, though of the sort that is generally put up after a man's death. He was now one of those rare Spaniards about whose distinction all Spaniards could agree. Yet the memorial itself was not to his taste. He never walked near those extravagant figures that would make his merits obvious in a world which had honoured him as though he were already defunct. He felt very much alive. However much his ideas belonged to the future, that broad-shouldered peasant figure in black clothes, with long arms and the clear grave eye of a Socrates, was part of the present. At seventy, Don Santiago was by no means an extinct volcano.

During the first World War Spain had kept her neutrality but she had still her own *guerilla* in Morocco. Then the revolving wheel of politics had brought back dictatorship under Don Miguel Primo de Rivera, an amiable though tempestuous ruler, and one of his acts was to curb the power of that *Junta para Ampliacion de los estudios*. That regime was indeed unfriendly towards Liberal ideas. The Rector of Salamanca University, Don Miguel de Unamuno, a Basque and writer of distinction, was exiled to the Canary Isles. The University of Madrid was closed for a year and a half. Spain was drifting towards an anarchy unknown for centuries. A political atmosphere of uncertainty and vague apprehension is the background for Cajal the philosopher as it has been for many another.

His own generation had enjoyed conditions more favourable for the intellectual life in Spain than any since the Golden Age. The Carlist wars when he was a youth, the Colonial rebellion, even that intermittent struggle with Moors in North Africa, had not greatly disturbed the life of the cafés, or prevented that free exchange of ideas which seemed to the men of Cajal's period the normal liberty of an educated person. Those Liberals might criticize the Church, but their wives went to Mass. Revolutionaries lived safely inside the Christian ethic.

At his *peña* in the café, Cajal was known for a man of independence, an anti-clerical, outspoken, unfriendly towards absolute power. Yet his fiery opinions never scorched; his weapons, though sharp, had no venom. He possessed the common touch, and it was no more possible to hate him than to hate a tree or a mountain. Beneath those sombre denunciations of Spanish inertia and neglect of science there was self-confident intellectual serenity. Unlike Unamuno the philosopher, Cajal was not exiled. He continued to philosophize, with a nineteenth-century tolerance. To those who had suffered an injury his advice was to contain themselves three days before reply: for on the first day, the pen was liable to be dipped in blood, on the second, in bile, but on the third day, they would use water — the symbol of calm, the best of all the colours. The extremist was not to his taste. 'Never argue with fanatics: we are not fighting a man but a formidable army, whose invisible soldiers, posted as a rearguard in space and time, cannot hear us.' Such freedom from fanaticism was beginning to be unfashionable in Spain as in other countries.

With the years, his personal Quixotism had grown

stronger, and his conception of the national hero more admiring. Like every Spaniard, he was impelled to make a pronouncement upon Don Quixote who is big enough to bear the most conflicting interpretations. Don Santiago had got over his disappointment as a boy on the first encounter with this famous book in the pastry-cook's attic. Yet, even now, it was hard for him to sympathize with the bitterness and pessimism that Cervantes had put into the figure of the hapless knight. He decided it was a case of compensation. The author knew poverty, hardship, Moorish slavery — yet his temperament remained serene and his philosophy equable. Cajal admired that Cervantean power of accepting the worst while believing the best. As for those who bewailed the fact that Spain had too many Quixotes, he declared that, on the contrary, there were too few. Spain needed more of those divine madmen seeking the impossible. Especially did science require their selfless dreaming.

Don Santiago had never ceased to formulate his opinions, and now it pleased him to collect them together and give them forth to the world. His life's work in histology was done. The *Instituto Cajal* had manifested that characteristic of maturity — the power to function independently of its parent. He might now look up from his working bench and speak to a larger audience, upon a wider theme. People were interested in him, and he was never hampered by undue self-reticence. His book of personal reminiscences, telling the story of the first part of his life had already provided material for the Cajal legend. Now, nearing seventy, he collected in a book those fragments of wisdom, paradoxes, barbed judgments and bitter-sweet aphor-

RAMON Y CAJAL—THE LAST PHASE

isms which had entertained his friends at the *Café Suizo*. In the recollection, those sayings pleased him. No doubt, as they came forth raw and molten from his lips, they had lacked form. No talk was ever as brilliant as when recollected in tranquililty. As he polished them in his mind, a connecting thread appeared. Like pieces of microscopic tissue, they looked much more convincing when arranged, and gradually, as he placed them together, these cultivated scraps were found to have grown into a philosophy, or at least a philosophic point of view. For the book, he chose an unpretentious, yet inspired title — *Charlas de Café* — Café conversations. It appeared in 1920, and in twelve years passed through four editions. Before another ten years, the *Charlas de Café* had been re-published, in a paper-covered book of 275 closely-printed pages, in Argentina, and in Mexico. Its appeal was not to any small coterie of intellectuals, but to a wide public of Spanish-speaking people.

The division of the chapters shows the range of the ideas. 1. Friendship, antipathies, ingratitude, hate. 2. Love and women. 3. Old age and anguish. 4. Concerning death, immortality, and glory. 5. Genius, talent, and foolishness. 6. Conversation, controversy. 7. Character, habit. 8. Teaching and education. 9. Direction in literature and art. 10. Politics, war, and social questions. 11. Jokes.

The final section proves the healthy balance of Cajal's mind.

To write aphorisms is a dangerous trade. Everything worth saying seems to have been said before. La Rochfoucauld and Blaise Pascal get in the way. Cajal was aware of these limitations, but no excessive veneration for the past had ever restrained him. He pointed out to his readers that even those masters of the epigram such as Montaigne, and La Bruyère had themselves often repeated ideas which had occurred in Plato, Horace and Plutarch. The fact is that the desire to compress truth in a phrase has been the ambition of wise men throughout the ages, and where Goethe and Stendhal have not completely succeeded, failure is not discreditable. Success depends on the degree of freshness that can be given to old themes. Cajal's aphorisms possess the Latin qualities of logic, intensity, drama. These pearls had been secreted in the oyster shell of his mind, and they are the final creative effort of the mountain boy who had made himself a scientist. Don Santiago looked back tolerantly upon that immature Crusoe.

When we come to the epigrams themselves we see how much Cajal is at home in this abbreviated form of expression. To suggest first of all the bouquet of these *pensées*, a few may be chosen at random.

'If you wish to leave behind something strong, true, beautiful, have the courage to write as though none of your contemporaries were to read you.'

'Friendship repels poverty as a flower repels darkness.'

'The social revolution is marching on. It is not difficult to imagine that sooner or later we shall all enjoy the same fraternity — of being poor.'

Upon the subject of love and women, Cajal writes with urbane irony. He quoted Renan: 'what a woman loves, God loves'. Yet only, he felt, in her early youth does a woman experience the genuine emotion of love. After that, her motive is ambition, and generally she grew old too early. To Cajal, these admired creatures represented rather a distraction in the life of a scientific man. He advised his pupils to marry one with modest tastes who would not interfere with his work, and he specially warned them against wealthy wives. A woman, he said, adores privilege, is little affected by injustice; whereas a man is capable of placing humanity before his family. Sometimes, the Moorish Pasha attitude of Don Santiago appears uppermost, and we remember that those café audiences were exclusively masculine. 'For a wise man an optimistic and happy wife will be treasured infinitely more than wealth.' We cry Hallelujah, and pass on. 'The misfortunes of marriage have their origin in the fact that the woman does not choose but is chosen.' It may be doubted whether that maxim is entirely valid for Anglo-Saxon countries. 'Nature offered woman chastity to make her strong and sane.' To that generalization, modern societies must provide many exceptions.

Such weary and worldly opinions, so patriarchal and traditional, tell us much about Cajal's thoughts and his background in nineteenth-century Spain where divorce was not countenanced. They speak of a conventional marriage, a happy outlook, and that innate masculine conservatism which had been so shocked by the lady reporters of New York.

Upon the subject of religion Cajal shows the opposite of that passionate Spanish emotion found in an Ignatius Loyola or a Teresa de Avila. 'Religion', he says, 'has not only a high moral worth, but a nutritional value. Faith develops and leads to enjoyable longevity, while doubt leads to pain in the soul and premature old age. If you do not believe in the soul, at least behave as though the soul existed.' What are we to make of so cautious a declaration of spiritual expediency? It reads like a thoroughly reliable prescription for staining sections. Even the scientist Louis Pasteur was a more spiritual man than Cajal. Yet though he did not possess the religious temperament, it has to be said that neither was he an atheist. That he should revolt against the authority of the Church is understandable; but in later life, he came even to question the laws of Darwin. Men of science often substitute for the dogmas of religion those of experiment, demanding absolute submission to scientific laws. But Cajal was no Grand Inquisitor of biology, though as Pio Baroja, the Basque novelist has said, he was something of a Rabbi. Sceptical materialism as an answer for unanswerable questions was the natural retreat of the nineteenth-century biologist; Cajal was different. He was a thoroughgoing determinist, but only at his working bench. He rose therefrom — and other aspirations took control. A faith based on severe rationalism could not explain to him the idiosyncrasies of living flesh. In every live organism there was a liveliness not to be expressed in scientific laws. Cajal laughed at the Vitalists — comparing them to the Chinese who had thought an automobile was animated by a horse inside its mechanism: but he could not avoid the challenge of that mysterious inwardness of living things. He knew that the pure sceptic never achieves anything except through the lapses of his scepticism. This intellectual child of Descartes and Isaac Newton, whose life's work had been in a sphere opposed to all mysticism, was not dehumanized by his science.

While he acknowledged that life was inexplicable, Cajal was also convinced of the biological value of death. The lower animals, it seemed to him, had remained fixed in their different species simply because they had no awareness of death, or at most only a crepuscular consciousness of it. For man, on the contrary, the terror of non-existence had become a major instrument of progress. Death had fashioned the hand, death had made the brain complex, and endowed man with his earliest tools. Death indeed was the source of life's intensity, and its existence was no reason for abnegating life.

Comparable in importance to a theory of death, is the problem of evil. For centuries it has worried the greatest philosophers. Cajal has a simple explanation, in terms of biology. Evil to him was merely a survival of animal instinct, a necessary consequence of the fact that one species has to nourish its vitality at the expense of others. Man himself is not-immune from this fundamental law. He must conquer his fellow men in order to flourish, and out of this grim necessity comes the permanence of evil in our lives. Our situation would be depressing, and perhaps hopeless, but for the fact that evil has its own value, its stimulating effect. Evil forms a motive for work, an incentive to curiosity. Just as death is necessary for life, so evil is a preservative against stagnation. Cajal saw this harsh fact in human life as a scavenging, almost a surgical agency.

Cajal is no systematic philosopher like Emanuel Kant. He wrote no textbook, offers no systematic theory as Henri Bergson does. Cajal is no more than a sage in sentences. He resembles Joseph Joubert, who wrote: 'I should like to make exquisite sense pass into commonsense, or make exquisite sense common', and who tortured himself to put a whole book into a phrase.

Someone has said the Spaniard is a shepherd by vocation, and a farmer by necessity. Caring for a scattered flock, rather than digging for truth, suited Cajal's temperament, and made him a philosophical nomad. The *Charlas de Café* show that philosophy need not be over-serious. We can dismiss his epigrams, or we can disagree with them, but they leave behind their taste, and among Spanish-speaking peoples, they have placed Ramon y Cajal the philosopher before readers who never heard of a neurone, and were quite indifferent to Cajal the histologist.

The last decade of Cajal's life saw more violent changes than Spain had known for centuries. When the dictator differed from his master Alfonso XIII and was obliged to retire, a dangerous vacuum occurred at the seat of power. A professor of philosophy, Ortega y Gasset, declared that the monarchy itself must be brought to an end. In the old mountain city of Jaca where Santiago had been taught and beaten by Fray Jacinto, an armed rebellion occurred which was a horrible foretaste of what was to come. In the general election of 1931, to the surprise of Spain, even of the Republicans, there was a large anti-monarchist majority in all the important towns and that summer, the last Bourbon monarch to reign in Europe passed into exile.

It was now the time for philosophy in action. The Liberals had come into their own. Ideas that Spain had resisted for generations were translated into law; legal equality for women; divorce; the abolition of teaching by the religious orders. The *Junta para Ampliacion de los estudios* went through a revival, and was able once more to send abroad promising students. Catalonia received more freedom than she had known for centuries. The theorist had his feast day.

In such an atmosphere Cajal published his last book.

It was called *El Mundo Visto a los Ochenta Años*, and he could not help adding the wryly humorous sub-title — 'the opinions of an arteriosclerotic'.

The book is a pastiche of scientific theories, biographical reminiscences, personal tastes. Cajal pours forth about the tribulations of old men, their infirmities, diminishing acuity of sense. He describes the various theories made to account for death and senility, including that of Elie Metchinkov who advised sour milk to counteract the fermentation in the large intestine which he thought to be the cause of ageing. Yet old men had their compensations, and found relief from their incapacities, as Beethoven and Goya had overcome the handicap of deafness. Cajal surveys the world, as it appeared to him in the 1930s, discusses the growth of cities, male and female dress. He gives warnings about the abuse of fresh air and the dangers of the modern cult of sunbathing. Whatever he has to say, he says emphatically, with his own accent. Maps and the tourist industry lead him to contrast the Spain of today unfavourably with that of yesterday. Art and particularly oil painting, is not what it was. In a majestic sweep, the philosopher completes the panorama of the world seen by an octogenarian, returns to the personal problem — the need to abstain from politics, his itch to write, his relief in photography, his return to the classic authors, with deliberate avoidance of anything likely to cause melancholy or excitement. The philosopher has become opinionated, even garrulous.

Yet it is not an old man's book. The reader feels the youthful spirit. Friends have spoken of Cajal's magnetic eyes, whether flashing, or still, they were never dull, and to look at the picture of the man of eighty is to imagine his voice, speaking still with traces of homely provincialism.

A few days before his death at 82, Goethe was still talking of self-improvement. But even Goethe did not write a book to describe his methods.

CHAPTER XXXVIII

CAJAL THE MAN

THOSE few decades which stretch back from the Goethean figure walking in the *Buen Retiro*, to the irrepressible Santiago slinging stones in a mountain village represent more than one man's life. They are a span of human development enough for several lives; and when we add the energetic years of Don Justo, we have the story of medicine from witchcraft to science. The father's experience dated back to those scarlet-robed figures the physicians, like him in Goya's picture *El Medico* who warms his hands in the fire of the *brasero* while he meditates on a passage out of those Latin folios at his side. How the Napoleon of surgery from Valpalmas despised such men! How fiercely he put before his boy a burning ideal of positive knowledge, based on anatomy; an ideal of craftsmanship with the scalpel, and a little blood-letting to impress the laity. That was Santiago's background, and his struggles to free himself from the father's aim, while keeping the father's inspiration, had caused him to shoot like a meteor away from all preconceived orbits.

What are the essentials in Cajal the man which enabled him to do this? Cajal the histologist is easy to understand — if one reads his books. A man's formal philosophy may be as dignified as his profile. We like to see him face to face, and catch the undisguised expression of his feelings. Those irreducible personal elements, the true raw material of his greatness form the most interesting parts of all. In Cajal they are not lofty or spiritual characteristics; on the contrary, his essentials are common and earthy.

If he were here to assist us in this character analysis (which would have interested him greatly) Cajal would have advised beginning with the background, pointing with pride to his descent from Aragon, a realm that antedated the kingdom of Spain. He would have described with affection those old Provençals who humanized medieval Europe. Those Aragonese, and Catalonians had less share in the three profound experiences that shaped the destiny of Spain — the Moorish conquest and reconquest, the Inquisition, and the colonization of America. Cajal's cosmopolitan instinct, his gift for languages, his practical energy look away from Spain, back to the Languedocean culture. Racial qualities are no more than tendencies, yet we cannot ignore their power. Heredity is a world of transmitted habits and compressed memories. Cajal would have insisted on their importance in shaping himself.

If pressed to mention his most outstanding quality, he would undoubtedly have said, 'My indomitable will power'. That phrase delighted him. He used it with the relish of a centenarian who ascribes his longevity to drinking cold water. Don Santiago would assume an oratorial posture, look back with self-admiration upon his early life. My hardships, my poverty, my triumph!

Certainly, his will power was strong. It had needed considerable resolve to shake free from his father. He inherited Don Justo's strength of character, but transformed it from the crude obstinacy of a peasant into an instrument of dynamic flexibility. Cajal always claimed for will power a sovereign omnipotence. Giving advice to research workers, he wrote: 'It might be said that work substitutes for talent, or better still that it creates talent.' To him, infirmity of will was equivalent to a disease, and in an entertaining chapter of the same book of advice, he analyses the various maladies of will on account of which some learned men fail to achieve distinction. His own power of concentration has been illustrated in this chronicle. It was partly the obsessive effect of accumulated effort. To get a result in hundreds, he used thousands. Another histologist would be content with a single preparation from one animal; Cajal examined the cat, the frog, the moth, the octopus, birds, mammals — every species he could find. Yet when it is admitted that Cajal had exceptional resolve, we are still left wondering exactly how the results came to be. Among simple people from the mountains, determination upon a fixed purpose is not rare, it is common, and even Don Justo's will did not take him beyond the anatomy rooms of Zaragoza.

Great men are often strangely deceived about their own strength. Cajal over-estimated the determination he inherited from Don Justo, and under-valued his own resilience and power of fancy; the faculty that soars upon wings of chance, which escapes unscathed from failure — a quality of wishful thinking that is always fresh, a faith self-renewing, independent of circumstance. This was his uniqueness. We have watched that mischievous boy, outmanœuvred by a justly enraged peasant, escape like a mountain wolf, then swiftly turn humiliation into victory. What charms us — and charmed the goddess Fortune — was his continuous adaptability, his creative resourcefulness. Nothing daunted the adventurous eagerness of either boy or man, neither his father's severity, nor Fray Jacinto's hunger technique, nor the Golgi stain. His penitence was brief, his recuperation rapid. It was mental audacity more than determination. It came from where strong-willed men are often deficient, namely the imagination. It went back to boyhood and Robinson Crusoe.

Out of his native power of fantasy came Cajal's aesthetic gift, which he invested with powerful emotions. The boy who climbed a dangerous way to pluck the rose of Alexandria was father to the man who saw the nerve cells as a row of daffodils and hyacinths. Artistic perception can register more delicately than any instrument of scientific precision. In every original investigation there comes the critical point when the experimenter reaches the end of what his apparatus can tell. He falls back upon the disciplined imagination which alone can guide him towards truth. What seems to be exact observation is nine-tenths discrimination, as we know from studying the visual apparatus. Objective reality is reached only through subjective interpretation. Those who teach students that science has no place for aesthetic gifts are showing them the way to mediocrity.

The richness of Cajal's artistic gift, as used in the service of histology, is revealed in his textbooks by those illustrations that were all drawn with his own hand. Though their subject matter is so very different, we may compare his representational method with that of the artist-naturalist J. J. Audubon whose great book adorned by magnificent pictures, about the birds of America appeared over a century ago.

At first sight, a lithograph by Audubon appears startling, even bizarre. That blue-winged teal scudding across the air against a background of sea and sky is like no bird we have ever seen. Each feather is revealed as clearly as a photograph — or so it seems. Then we realize on close inspection that the artist has only drawn a few of the feathers, but has thereby made us understand the design of the wings, tail and head in a way more convincing than any camera. The same with other features of the bird. Audubon's pictures are accurate but they possess what is more important than accuracy, namely truthfulness. Later observers of birds are perhaps more scientific — but none has given a clearer idea of bird reality.

Cajal's gift of illustration transmutes the chaos of the microscopic slide into a clear representation for the eye and the mind. It is no accident that his drawings have the quality of fine etchings: yet no one has ever proved them inaccurate. Histologists of the future will use different techniques — electrical and chemical — and will find out new aspects of the living cells. No one will ever make histology more alive.

Having allowed Cajal the inventiveness of Robinson Crusoe and the transcribing faculty of Audubon, we come to another gift. His ability to impose his ideas upon others. It was a species of high-powered telepathy. Once this is understood, the relationship between Santiago and his stern father becomes comprehensible, even touching. Don Justo provided the force, but his boy contributed the illumination — once he had learned the trick. His eyes coolly measured each look upon the father's features, penetrating the next move, judging exactly how far he might go. And Dr. Ramon, so sceptical and so obtuse, so full of ideas and so deficient in feeling, was taken in by his son's resourcefulness. He swallowed that tale about the pigeon loft, and many another effort of his son's ingenious fancy. Santiago's spell over him grew stronger, and its triumph came when Don Justo abruptly realized — for such an unimaginative man it was a mental thunderbolt — that drawing could be used in the service of anatomy. By that time, his son had grown beyond him. That was the father's tragedy. Santiago's intense power of making fantasy real, and of imposing it upon others grew stronger, until it could fascinate men like von Kölliker and a whole conference of European histologists. It was not merely the leadership that a man of strong ideas radiates in any group; it was a power resembling mesmeric compulsion, like the influence which some people have over animals or children.

Don Santiago had in the days of his celebrity the same skilful management of the world. He was a Liberal, an agnostic. Yet he remained unharmed by the hand of authority because of the protective aura cast by his personal authority. The same magnetic domination has survived his death. He has been posthumously honoured by the Spanish Government, and the centenary of his birth has become a national celebration. Yet his career represents tendencies that are not typical of Spain.

Some admirers have marvelled that Cajal achieved what he did without proper schooling, and no laboratory training. But educated people always over-value the importance of education. Santiago Ramon had one of those lucky minds which teach themselves and are harmed by pedagogy. He learned through the stimulus of opposition and preserved the freshness of a virgin mind. As for technical training, there could be no better way than the way instinct made him follow. Even the barber and the cobbler had taught him something. When nature intends an individual for a pioneer journey, she equips him with nothing but the desire, and lets him find his own way. If Ramon y Cajal had been born later, and been awarded one of those travelling Fellowships by the *junta*, his career might have been different, but his work could hardly have been finer. He would have picked up methods in some German laboratory, but he might have been content to learn instead of being obliged to invent.

Cajal said he chose histology because it was the poor man's study, needing no expensive apparatus. Poverty of means had been to him no bar to achievement. 'There are no exhausted subjects, only exhausted men. Nearly all those who have no confidence in their own powers do not know the marvellous power of prolonged attention.' That was his teaching. The material was cheap, but the craftsmanship was superfine. In Spain, where water, grass, soil and trees are scarce and represent wealth in a sense more favoured countries cannot understand, poverty and necessity often act like narcotics. Cajal wished to make them stimulate the improvising, inventing, creative faculties of his countrymen.

He had made good use of the raw material of himself, though like every man, he was full of inconsistencies. The Quixotic dreamer balanced the rude craftsman. About his work, he was over-serious, yet in the café, he was exceedingly good company. He had a large appetite for life, yet in food and drink he was abstemious, and did not smoke. A prophet of gloomy forebodings — he faced the ordinary events of life with an engaging simplicity. Don Santiago — a great man, yes. But also very much of a child.

Alas, those mental intensities of his were not developed without sacrifice. Cajal was at home with what he could see, and feel, and touch. When he used a razor to cut a section, his fingers instinctively judged the correct degree of pressure. By study and reflection too he became at home with ideas. But he was out of his depth with the minds of average men. They were enigmas to him. The cynicism of some of his sayings suggests unworldliness. That freshness of gaze which he brought to life was not to be purchased except at the cost of a certain innocence. We have seen how the politician Don Segismundo handled him. There was another man of affairs, the great Emilio de Castelar, the Radical statesman who had once been President of Spain during that brief first Republic, when Cajal was a student at Zaragoza. For years, Castelar had been to him almost a demigod; eloquent, patriotic, impressive — a man without defects. One day in the café, Cajal was dumbfounded to be told what was common knowledge, that this illustrious statesman had another side to his nature. Cajal heard with astonishment that his idol was a notorious spendthrift, and not over-scrupulous. Castelar was believed on one occasion to have abused his great position to allow a man charged with murder to evade justice — because he owed that man money. Cajal was bitterly disappointed in his hero.

Yet Castelar's human failings were common knowledge in the cafés of Madrid, and those *contertulios* who sat admiringly at Don Santiago's table listening to his profound and humorous wisdom had been more perceptive than he, because less blinded by idealism.

It was fortunate that Ramon y Cajal never deserted science to make a career in affairs.

CHAPTER XXXIX

CAJAL'S INFLUENCE

THE epic conclusion to a great man's life is no more than the end of the beginning. He dies, then after a brief post-mortem oblivion, he rises again. A completely new personality makes a first modest appearance. The man whom posterity recognizes is not the man his contemporaries knew. A similar decomposition and recomposition takes place in his work. Great discoveries become merged in the substance of human knowledge. Louis Pasteur's work has become the possession of the human race, and later ages will have difficulty in recalling how it came to pass.

Cajal knew that posterity places a different price upon achievement. The fate of another man born in Aragon, Miguel Servet, whom the world knows as Servetus, was a tragic instance of this strange transvaluation. Servetus had studied at Toulose, had followed medicine in Paris, and practised as a physician. But his heart was not in medicine. He was a ferocious controversialist, who attacked both Catholics and Protestants, but especially the mighty John Calvin, the theocrat of Geneva against whom he directed his great book of theology, the *Christianismi Restitutio*. In the course of his argument, the intemperate Servetus, who was a veritable Quixote of rashness, happened to remember an observation derived from his younger days as a pupil of Vesalius the anatomist. He used a few brief lines to explain — merely as an illustration of his theological argument — that the circulating blood, when it has passed through the lungs, is of a bright red colour, because it contains air. It was no more than a casual allusion. To Servetus the theology was momentous, and this reference to the blood quite incidental. Yet those few unheeded lines form the first written reference to a cardinal fact of physiology — the aeration of blood in the lungs. The unhappy Servetus did not understand the magnitude of that pregnant anticipation, neither did such a point interest his malignant enemy. John Calvin, into whose power he came, put Servetus to the stake at Geneva, and used copies of his books to kindle the flames of martyrdom. He would not have been prepared to die for his theory of the pulmonary circulation, yet it is this which has made him live.

Cajal quoted the episode of Servetus to illustrate that an innovator is only half aware of what he is doing. It is likely that the future will rewrite Cajal's own life, and arrange his merits in a different order.

Long before his death, Ramon y Cajal was a popular hero of Spain.

In troublous times, when even to wear a collar is to be suspected of anti-democratic principles, he drew the homage of the common people. His Socratic face appeared on postage stamps and banknotes; it looked down upon the *Madrilenos* from a column of stone. An American unable to make himself understood on his arrival in the Spanish capital, mentioned he had come to study with Cajal — and at once, all doors were opened.

Yet a visitor to the *Instituto Cajal* would seek the master in vain in the laboratories there. He had never been quite at home at those well-equipped benches, preferring the plain working place in his own home. His room seemed so uninspiring, until the eye saw around the walls that gallery of original drawings that were the old masters of histology. His aversion from the new building was prophetic of something fate had in store.

His everyday existence must have been lonely in those years, for Señora Cajal and several of their children had died earlier. His wife did not seem to participate in the external features of his career. A 'true Spanish woman', as he was pleased to call her, she preferred her own *patio*, secluded from gaze, where she presided over her family, in the happy marriage which has no history. She kept apart from his professional life, though enveloped in him. It was as unlike as possible the desires of those American ladies whose love for independence had astonished her. The shy little thing with honey-coloured plaits who fell in love with the bandit schoolboy belonged to him to the day of her death. It was she who drew him from beneath Don Justo's authoritarian wing, and brought him independence and good luck. Don Santiago, referring to the power of a contented home life as a background to a scientific career, writes with a graciousness that rings true.

In those last years, one of his pupils from the New World, a brain surgeon, Wilder Penfield paid a visit in company with Pio del Rio Hortega who had now been reconciled to the master. They found the old man sitting upright in bed, his manuscripts all around him, and the wall bespattered with ink from his impatient pen. The volcano gave threatening puffs, and now and then a discharge. Cajal had become hard of hearing, and his body had grown feeble, yet the mind blazed out from the expressive eyes below shaggy eyebrows. With gestures he discussed his current article in which that old heresy of the 'network' was being refuted once more. Infirm in body, but lively in mind, he was a living proof of his own teaching that the brain cells do not grow old as quickly as other tissues.

Yet even in that final utterance of his histological faith — the paper upon the neurones he discussed with his visitors — Cajal kept the open-mindedness of a philosopher. 'We are neither dogmatic nor exclusive — Neuronal discontinuity, though proved in numerous instances, might have exceptions.' It was magnificent. It was the same as saying that his life's work might prove to have been a mistake.

About old age, Cajal was quite unsentimental. The café conversations have an aphorism on the subject. 'In youth, we say, I am immortal. In old age, we say, I die without having lived. It would be the same if we lived the three hundred years of the crocodile, or the two hundred of the elephant.' He had no self-commiseration, none of that dread of death and desire to prolong life beyond the grave in which a typical Spaniard finds compensation for his austere life on earth. In the *Charlas de Café* he wrote sardonically; 'You amount to very little if your death is not desired by many.'

His own journey to the grave was a grand affair, a cortège followed by thousands who had never heard of neurones, yet with a popular instinct to share in this celebration of greatness, had grasped that Don Santiago had somehow contributed to the pride which every Spaniard might feel merely in the fact of being Spanish. Cajal would have understood the motives for their homage. Spain is a land where the country counts for more than the city. He was himself a countryman, and knew how peasants enjoy a burying. His sharp wit would have punctured any exaggerated reverence over the circumstances of a man's death. He had written: 'In the pomp of a funeral the only beings who seem to appreciate the solemnity of the occasion and to abstain from gossiping about the deceased are the horses.'

The citizens of Madrid followed the black plumes and attended the funeral Mass. Peasants in Aragon and Navarre heard of their compatriot's passing — yes, he was old Don Justo's clever son, and his mother had been Antonia Cajal, from up the valley of the Gallego. Histologists all over the world discussed his reputation.

In the roll of the deceased Fellows of the Royal Society of London, Charles Scott Sherrington put his finger upon the reason for Cajal's popularity at home and abroad. 'His scientific devotion and prestige were taken to typify what a new Spain might cherish and accomplish. He was a forecast of what a new Spain might stand for.'

'A new Spain' — that phrase of Sherrington's corresponds to Cajal's own vision of the 'Spanishness' which was still to be born, once the true genius of the people were awakened. Cajal translated *Hispanidad* not into bygone tradition based upon race and religion. To him it was a new aspect of the greatness of his race based upon the development of science, something in which a man from Aragon and a man of Buenos Aires or Lima as well as from old Spain could feel a common share. To the last day of his life Cajal dreamed of restoring those riches which had been lost in the sea, those talents which had been spoiled by ignorance; so that the modern world should esteem Spain for more than the wines of Jerez and the music of Granados.

Was this nothing more than mere innate Quixotism, an illusion of the eye that sees giants in windmills and golden caskets in barber's bowls?

Cajal had been two years in his grave before the outbreak of the worst civil war that Spain has ever known. His death mask in the *Instituto Cajal* stared up from among its draperies, serenely unaware of the tragedy, and the very building itself became an artillery post, as though testifying to his own conviction that grandeur does not accord with the spirit of science.

This war was no mere quarrel between one province and another. It was a conflict of fundamental passions, conducted with a new technique of scientific barbarism. The rest of Europe shuddered complacently over the malady which had overtaken Spain, though feeling premonitory symptoms of the same disease. What had those intellectuals in the *Calle de Alcala* been discussing over their coffee cups that they failed to prevent this catastrophe? Had the intellectuals counted too much on the authority of reason? Probably. Yet if we are not to hope for the triumph of rational illumination, what is to become of the human race? They were inadequate, those café talkers, but they did not entirely lack vision.

A summary of Cajal's posthumous influence may explain what his age taught its successor. His influence can be detected in two quite separate spheres: the first being in the field where the human brain has attempted to construct an imitation of itself— an artificial brain; the second in clinical medicine and surgery.

Since man learned from histology that brain is a machine, he has attempted to make other brains in his own image. The so-called electronic calculator or electric brain has some of the features of a human cerebrum. It is an enormous mass of valves and wires. In making it, the physicist has reproduced those nerve arrangements which Cajal studied under the microscope.

The machine's valves and switches have a strong functional likeness to neurones, although in its present state the electronic computor is to be compared more to invertebrates than to man, whose neurones number ten thousand million as compared with the machine's twenty thousand valves. A mathematical problem, that would take a man weeks or months to resolve, is presented to the machine. Currents pass, valves light up, the vast electrical organism becomes alive — and the solution of the problem is delivered in a few minutes. The electronic calculator has even a certain limited faculty of remembering, or rather of retaining. More extraordinary however, is that these machines are prone to breakdowns which have a strong resemblance to human diseases. Even more astonishing the fact that such electronic aberrations can be 'cured' by shaking the machine, or by passing through it a cleansing charge of electricity, in much the same way as 'shock treatment' is applied in human psychiatry.

This 'electronic brain' which can outstrip the human mind in mathematics, and shows this sinister tendency to imitate man's deficiencies as well — might it not also aspire to man's higher functions? Is there a risk that mechanical brains might develop the will-to-leadership? Our generation has good reason to ask that disturbing question, which comes up so unexpectedly as part of the fruits of brain histology.

Fortunately, the danger of an electronic Frankenstein master, or cerebral robot, using man's own knowledge to make him a slave, seems remote. A Chicago physicist has said that a machine possessing the same number of units as does the human brain would require the Empire State Building to house it, and the electrical output of

Niagara to drive it. Even the finest machine has no power to initiate, no genuine memory, no command over ideas. Human control is needed to present the problems, operate the switch, and repair the breakdowns. Brain histology has not been leading us towards a super cerebrum.

Cajal was a long way from understanding the metaphysical functions of brain. Yet one day — his plan of the warp and woof of the tissues might help mankind to understand the intentions of the great spinner who designed the pattern.

The second and more humane service that Cajal's work has brought to modern man — is the relief given in organic brain diseases.

The remote and invisible brain, secure in its box of skull, has always fascinated surgeons. Primitive exponents of that craft centuries ago ventured to make small doorways in the bone, with their exceedingly rude instruments. Even when antisepsis and anaesthesia made cranial surgery safe, the brain surgeon was like a traveller without a map, and his perilous journeys were justified only by grave need. Brain histology has altered all that. Blank spaces in the brain map have been filled in with positive knowledge. The operator knows where he is going, and what he may expect to find. He traces the cause of a disturbance to its exact place inside the skull within millimetres. Merely cutting some of those microscopic nerve fibres has been found to produce beneficial effects in mental diseases. Tumours, swellings no bigger than the size of a pea, can be located and removed. Thanks to histology, their mode of growth and spread has been studied as though they were plants in a greenhouse. That *microglia*, the connecting jelly of del

Rio Hortega, which Cajal had overlooked, has been found especially liable to develop abnormal growths. Confidence — increasing over fifty years — is what microscopic knowledge has given to the practising surgeon. Had Don Justo Ramon been born a century later, he would have been proud to salute those modern Napoleons of the brain whose practical success is based on anatomy. Of this microscopic world, his son Santiago was the Columbus.

The continuing influence of Ramon y Cajal after his death in 1934 can be expressed in the brief story of an American surgeon, one of the latest of those pilgrims who found inspiration at the *Instituto Cajal* during the master's lifetime. His name is Wilder Penfield, and like Cajal, a doctor's son.

He was born at the extreme north-west of the United States, overlooking that ocean which a Spanish sailor named *El Pacifico*, at the furthest limit of the territories which the Conquistadores reached. The Penfield forebears had pushed westward to these ultimate boundaries. But he himself became a nomad in the reverse direction, searching out the best in several countries in diligent self-education to become a surgeon. At Princeton University, under Woodrow Wilson, at Johns Hopkins, at Oxford, where he was a Rhodes scholar, and under Charles Scott Sherrington, Penfield worked at those basic sciences that make a surgeon fit for his work. Wilder Penfield was a pioneer who relied on his own judgment. Drawn by the fame of Cajal, he came to Madrid, although his American friends were highly sceptical over the likelihood of anything good being found in Spain.

There was deep feeling in the master's voice as he

received his American admirer in the library of the *Instituto Cajal*. He poured out his old grievance that scientists would not learn Spanish, and were discovering anew what had been described years before in the *Trabajos*. After his own death, he told Wilder Penfield, the Spanish school of histology would pass away. His head was fallen on his chest so that only white hair and beard were to be seen as a halo for the large eyes. The next time he saw Cajal there was an even greater contrast between mental energy and bodily decrepitude.

From the *Instituto Cajal* and the tradition of its creator Wilder Penfield had learned much. He had justified the originality of his choice. Henceforth his professional life was absorbed wholly in the surgery of the nervous system which another American, Harvey Cushing, had carried to a high point of skill. Twenty years after his sojourn in Madrid, Wilder Penfield has become the leading brain surgeon in the world, Professor at McGill University, Montreal, and a member of that exceedingly small, unique body, the *Order of Merit*, who are chosen personally by the British Sovereign. He is the first practising doctor to be so honoured since Lord Lister.

Ramon y Cajal would have found satisfaction in that successful career, although to him the pure science was more dear than its application. It would have pleased him that neurones, *axons*, and *microglia*, so faithfully studied in Spain had opened a new realm for the healing art. Pleasure would have come from the thought that this development of his own life's work had flowered through a man born at the extreme north-west of America, the furthest limit of the province of New Spain. Wilder Penfield's fertilization with an idea — was that not proof of the vitality of *Hispanidad*? A confirmation of his Quixotic dream that Spain of the future would have her scientific *conquistadores*, as once she had produced her soldiers, priests and rulers.

In October 1944, on the tenth anniversary of the master's death two pupils — Pio del Rio Hortega, and Clemente Estable, Professors respectively in Buenos Aires and Montevideo, gave moving orations upon his personality, now admired wherever Spanish is spoken, just as his work belongs to all medicine.

The modern Spanish writer Azorin denounces the idea that Spain is 'decadent', pointing to the twenty nations of America which Spain created with help from no one, and endowed with her language. But to Cajal, the past was not enough; he desired to add to those twenty nations, twenty sciences also.

We cannot foresee what the future will make of the raw material of this great man's career. Perhaps in days to come it is not histology, or even the brain that will keep his name alive. His discoveries will have become part of the general stock of knowledge. It may be that Spaniards of the twenty-first century, both in the Old World and the New, will remember the Aragonese Ramon y Cajal not as a biologist but as a writer of epigrams, and mouthpiece of typically Spanish wisdom, more of a Lope de Vega than a Louis Pasteur.

REFERENCES

José Alvarez-Sierra: *Ramon y Cajal*. Editora Nacional, Graficos Uguina, Melendes Valdes 7, Madrid, 1951.

Azorin: *An Hour of Spain Between 1560 and 1590*. Jonathan Cape, 1933, translated by Alice Raleigh.

Dorothy F. Cannon: *Explorer of the Human Brain; The Life Story of Santiago Ramon y Cajal (1852-1934)*. Schuman, New York, 1949.

Miguel Dolc: *Ramon y Cajal en el Instituto de Huesca*. Huesca, 1952.

Havelock Ellis: *The Soul of Spain*. Constable, 1929.

Clemente Estable: *An Article on Ramon y Cajal*. El Dia. Montevideo, December 28th, 1952.

Richard Ford: *Gatherings From Spain*. London, 1846.

José Ortega y Gasset: *Invertebrate Spain*. G. Allen & Unwin, 1937.

Theophile Gautier: *A Romantic in Spain*. Alfred Knopf, New York, 1926.

Charles R. Gibson, F.R.S.E.: *The Romance of Modern Photography*. Seeley Service & Co. Ltd., 38 Great Russell Street, London, 1919.

Miguel de Cervantes Saavedra, translated by Charles Jervais: *Don Quixote*, 1617.

Geoffrey Jefferson: *The Mind of Mechanical Man*. Lister Oration delivered June 9th, 1949. *British Medical Journal*, June 25th, 1949, vol. I.

Ernest Jones: *Sigmund Freud, his life and work*, vol. I, London, 1953. The Hogarth Press.

Esmond R. Long: *History of Pathology*. Baillière, Tindall & Cox, London, 1928.

REFERENCES

Los Angeles Neurological Society, Bulletin, May 1st, 1952: *Cajal Centenary Number.* Los Angeles, 1952.

Gregorio Maranon: *Cajal, Su Tiempo Y el Nuestro.* Espasa Calpe, S.A., Madrid, 1951.

W. H. McMenemey: *Santiago Ramon y Cajal.* Proceedings of the Royal Society of Medicine, Vol. XLVI, 173 (October 21st, 1952).

E. Allison Peers: *Catalonia Infelix.* Methuen, 1937.

Wilder Penfield: *Cranial Clues to Intracranial Abnormality.* Caldwell Lecture, 1951. *American Journal of Roentgenology,* April 1952.

Wilder Penfield: *Santiago Ramon y Cajal.* Archives of Neurology and Psychiatry, January 1935, vol. XXXIII, pp. 172-3 (American Medical Association, Chicago).

Wilder Penfield: *The Career of Ramon y Cajal.* Archives of Neurology and Psychiatry, August 1926, vol. XVI, pp. 213-20. (American Medical Association, Chicago).

Pio Baroja: *Galeria de Tipos de la Epoca.* 1947.

Pio del Rio Hortega and Clemente Estable: *Ramon y Cajal.* Homenaje en el decimo aniversario de su muerte, Octubre 1944. Montevideo.

Princess Pilar of Bavaria and Desmond Chapman-Houston: *Don Alfonso XIII.* John Murray, 1931.

Georges Potonniee: *Histoire de la Decouverte de la Photographie.* Publications Photographiques Paul Montel, 35 Boulevard Saint-Jacques, Paris, 1925.

Santiago Ramon y Cajal: Cuadernos Biograficos, Ediciones de la Direccion General de Relaciones Culturales, Madrid, 1952.

Santiago Ramon y Cajal: *Charlas de Café.* Espasa Calpe Argentina, S.A.

Santiago Ramon y Cajal: *El Mundo Visto a los Ochenta Años.* Espasa Calpe Argentina, S.A.

REFERENCES

Santiago Ramon y Cajal: *Degeneration and Regeneration of the Nervous System*. Oxford University Press, London, Humphrey Milford, 1928.

Santiago Ramon y Cajal: *Histology*. Baillière, Tindall & Cox, London, 1933.

Santiago Ramon y Cajal: *Precepts and Counsels on Scientific Investigation: Stimulants of the Spirit*. Ed. Cyril B. Courville, M.D., Pacific Press Publishing Association, Mountain View, California, 1951.

Santiago Ramon y Cajal: *Recollections of My Life*. Memoirs of the American Philosophical Society, volume VIII, parts 1 and 2, Philadelphia, 1937, translated by Prof. Horne Craigie with the assistance of Prof. Juan Cano.

C. S. Sherrington: *Santiago Ramon y Cajal*. Obituary Notices of Fellows of the Royal Society, no. 4, 1935.

J. B. Trend: *The Origins of Modern Spain*. Cambridge University Press, 1934.

Joseph Trueta: *The Spirit of Catalonia*. Oxford University Press, London, 1946.

Miguel de Unamuno: *Essays and Soliloquies*. Harrap, 1925.

Louis N. Wilson: *Memoir of Dr. Hall*. Clark University Publications, vol. VII.